Write!
A Guide *for*
Graduate Nursing Students
and Professionals

Joyce E. Johnson, PhD, RN, NEA-BC, FAONL, FAAN
Conway School of Nursing
The Catholic University of America
Washington, D.C.

Kevin M. Rulo, PhD, MA, BA
Department of English
University Writing Center
The Catholic University of America
Washington, D.C.

DES*tech* Publications, Inc.

Write! A Guide for Graduate Nursing Students and Professionals

DEStech Publications, Inc.
439 North Duke Street
Lancaster, Pennsylvania 17602 U.S.A.

Printed in the United States of America
10   9   8   7   6   5   4   3   2   1

Main entry under title:
    Write! A Guide for Graduate Nursing Students and Professionals

A DEStech Publications book
Bibliography: p.
Includes index p. 227

Library of Congress Control Number: 2020949394
ISBN No. 978-1-60595-510-0

HOW TO ORDER THIS BOOK

BY PHONE: 877-500-4337 or 717-290-1660, 9AM–5PM Eastern Time

BY FAX: 717-509-6100

BY MAIL: Order Department
DEStech Publications, Inc.
439 North Duke Street
Lancaster, PA 17602, U.S.A.

BY CREDIT CARD: American Express, VISA, MasterCard, Discover

BY WWW SITE: http://www.destechpub.com

*To nurses who aim to elevate their writing proficiency,
excel in the academic and practice environments,
and disseminate knowledge to improve clinical
outcomes and advance the profession.*

Table of Contents

SECTION II

SECTION III

SECTION V

Preface

UNIVERSITIES have responded to the 2010 call from the Institute of Medicine for doubling the number of nurses with doctoral degrees by 2020. Although the steep growth in the number of PhD and doctor of nursing practice (DNP) programs continues to impress academicians, the sharp increases in enrollments have challenged nursing faculty to accommodate the large numbers of nurses who have begun the long process of obtaining an advanced degree. Faculty now welcome an ever-increasing number of new students into on-campus or online programs each semester. Courses commence, students submit written assignments, and then the challenge begins: addressing the students' writing proficiency shortfalls.

A similar scenario unfolds for the nurse author who submits a manuscript for publication in a professional journal. The editor acknowledges the article's innovative content, but the ability of the writer to convey the content logically, clearly, and concisely falls seriously short, and the editor rejects the manuscript. Why does this happen?

The simple answer is that the focus of undergraduate nursing education has been to enable nursing students to acquire technical knowledge sufficient to practice nursing safely. As a result, most academic nursing programs require few written assignments, and certainly none that rise to the level of a professional publication. In addition, the clinical setting now values "point and click" in clinical charting, which has diminished the need for written nurses' notes. It is no wonder that nurses who enter graduate programs experience serious shock when professors return assignments with low scores because of poor writing skills, or when editors reject manuscripts that are poorly written and unreadable.

We wrote this handbook to help solve these problems for nurses who are beginning or already enrolled in graduate degree programs, as well as those interested in successfully publishing. The book—a collaborative professional endeavor—is unique because it is customized for nurses. The content will help writers create clear, concise, and accurate manuscripts and articles that meet exacting professional standards.

We do not suggest that professional writing is easy or requires little effort. On the contrary, writing professionally is a process that requires stepping outside of one's comfort zone, learning new techniques, and, most of all, demonstrating the willingness to practice new skills until the final product is ready for publication. We have embedded practical steps in each chapter that address writing mechanics and believe that through careful reflection and regular practice, even weak writers can quickly improve the quality of their writing.

This textbook provides a practical, easy-to-use, systematic reference for helping *all* nurses improve their writing skills, whether they are students in graduate nursing programs, nursing faculty, program directors, nurse educators, nurse clinicians, nurse executives, or APRNs. This text responds to three problems in nursing today: faculty frustration with poor graduate student writing that detracts from learning course content; student frustration and/or failure from technical writing deficiencies; and lack of readily available, easy-to-use tools that can actually improve student writing skills. In contrast to the numerous, generic writing tutorials available today, this text stands alone because the content is tailored to the graduate nursing experience.

In Section I, we make a convincing case for why good writing matters in nursing today and in the future; underscore writing competency emphasis of organizations that accredit nursing graduate programs; and tackle the rhetorical triangle, genre, and discourse as well as intention or purpose. In Section II, we detail the critical differences and similarities among the writing requirements of three terminal degrees in nursing. We also explain the rationale for and steps in conducting an audience analysis; the critical importance of beginnings and endings; and the power of engaging the audience through story development. Section III includes the classic "nuts and bolts"—those essential tools needed to write with correct English, use more powerful words, *and* elevate your personal level of writing. In Section IV, we included practical information about the *process* of writing and collaborating with co-authors, independent editors and writing coaches, and editors of professional journals. Section V addresses the importance of knowledge dissemination and in Chapter 12, we address the "now what" question by offering a number of specific action steps that will help you leverage available resources to elevate your writing proficiency.

We dedicate this textbook to all nurses. We acknowledge that writers have their own voices and that these voices are in part disciplinary and related to the field of knowledge and discourse communities within the academy. Chapter 3 and Chapter 6 reflect both his disciplinary voice and practices from English. With commitment and continued practice, the lessons learned in this book can last a lifetime and enable nurses at all levels and in all clinical venues to disseminate their learned knowledge to improve clinical outcomes and advance the nursing profession.

Now . . . on to "Write"!

Acknowledgments

To our friends, family, and academic colleagues whose encouragement in support of improving writing proficiency enabled our vision to become a reality.

My sincere appreciation to my co-author, Dr. Kevin Rulo, for giving me yet another opportunity to work with him as we endeavor to assist nurses to improve their writing proficiency.

My sincere appreciation to my son, Jeff, and my daughter-in-law, Paria, for their support and encouragement in this latest textbook development adventure.

To the many students who have suffered through "be" verb elimination in my courses: *thank you* for the hard work you invested in learning a new writing style, *thank you* for loving to learn, and *thank you* for preparing yourselves for the many writing adventures that await you during your professional careers.

Joyce E. Johnson

Introduction

WHEN my son attended Gonzaga College High School in Washington, DC, he would bring home new academic challenges and spend each evening trying to master new course content through homework assignments. I doubt that he delighted in tackling the assignments, but, like others in his class, he dutifully plodded through each one and usually completed them by dinner.

On one afternoon, however, his efforts fell short and so did his temper. When his frustration reached a tipping point, I/Mom stepped in to help and provide support. He related that his English teacher no longer permits students to use any weak copulatives in their written assignments. Copulatives? What are copulatives? I certainly did not know, but I soon learned that copulatives are verbs, and that he could no longer use any form of the verb "to be" because his teacher considered them "weak" verbs. My son declared that he no longer could write anything of substance because "I just can't write without using 'be' verbs!" That evening, we both began the journey of writing in the active voice, without "be" verbs—a journey that changed his writing style and my writing proficiency for the better, forever.

"Be" verbs include "is, was, am, are, were, be, being, been, can, must, might . . . and many more "weak" verbs. Excluding and/or minimizing the use of "be" verbs invites use of the *active voice* (rather than the passive voice) preferred in scholarly writing. Early in my academic tenure, I required that my students fully *eliminate* the use of "be" verbs and write in the active voice. What prompted this rubric requirement?

When I moved from the healthcare administrative practice setting to academia, I encountered what academicians in universities throughout the nation encounter daily—poorly developed writing skills in undergraduate and graduate students. Nowhere does poor writing affect student performance more than in graduate and post-graduate programs. Here, students must demonstrate technical and grammatical mastery, but equally important, they must learn how to navigate new genres and how to integrate complex research into writing. They must gain the confidence as writers to assume authority in the midst of a variety of voices and views. They must become fluent in the more demanding forms of academic discourse of the professional nursing researcher and scholar as they write doctor of nursing practice (DNP) projects, PhD dissertations, and potentially scholarly publications. Many, if not most, students find it difficult to achieve this level of writing. Student and faculty frustration and/or student failure often result when students fall short of meeting professor and university writing expectations.

Dr. Rulo and I believe, however, that every nursing graduate student can succeed in becoming an effective writer, and we developed this textbook to guide the graduate student toward that goal. This book provides the tools and strategies to ensure that kind of success. We address every writing need and every aspect of the writing process in one volume—including communicating effectively in any situation, understanding the genres and discourses of the profession, collaborating with colleagues, and developing manuscripts that present their materials in a compelling and professionally astute manner. While writing books abound, we developed this academic textbook specifically for use by graduate nursing students and/or graduate nursing faculty to support and advance their writing proficiency. In addition, this book also aims to provide nursing academicians with a usable resource and tool to assist graduate nursing students to master writing techniques and excel in the academic setting. With *Write! A Guide for Nursing Graduate Students and Professionals*, students have a one-stop shop for becoming full-fledged writers and even, we could say, complete nurses—since you can't be a complete nurse-scholar-leader if you can't research and disseminate that research, develop your thinking and communicate your ideas, persuade others to adopt the courses of action that you recommend, and represent the field with tact and elegance.

As the readers journey through our chapters, they will find that we underscore the *commitment* necessary to acquire and/or enhance writing skill sets. Committing to elevating writing proficiency takes focus and hard work, but when properly executed, the writing product will rank second to none. We readily acknowledge that the writing process is *messy*, from pre-writing and drafting to editing and revising but, with practice, it becomes easier and (eventually) enjoyable. We underscore that effective communication involves persuasion. Therefore, understanding the intended audience emerges as most important. We offer examples of exemplar writing in masters Capstone Project Papers, DNP Scholarly Project papers, and PhD dissertations, believing that viewing well-written narratives can enlighten and enable others to elevate their personal writing proficiency. Exposure to models of good writing expands the writer's sense for what is possible and endows the writer with a greater reservoir of expression from which to draw. Framing a manuscript includes emphasizing the importance of a *beginning* and an *ending*. Applying these strategies, even a novice writer can develop a worthy manuscript and convey content accurately, clearly, and concisely. Finally, we also offer the "nuts and bolts" of grammatically correct writing by centering on the most common writing errors and snafus that trip up even an experienced writer.

In case you wonder if today I permit students in my courses to use "be verbs," the answer is no. Initially, they struggle—just like my son did—and some become angry and frustrated with the required extra effort. However, those students who love to learn, and those who desire to prepare themselves for whatever professionally unfolds, master the skill. In the process, they permanently elevate their personal writing proficiency, ready themselves for whatever future writing adventure awaits, and create written narratives with clarity, style, and grace.

SECTION I

CHAPTER 1

Why Good Writing Matters in Nursing Today

"It ain't whatcha write, it's the way atcha write it."
—Jack Kerouac, WD

Introduction

IN a 1960 textbook written for aspiring student nurses, Morison set forth the standards, principles, competencies, adjustments, relationships, professional and civic opportunities, social and economic foundations, ethics, and religious considerations that comprised nursing practice at the time. According to Morison, these requirements for the practice of nursing built upon the principles recommended by Florence Nightingale, which led to the establishment of the first American schools of nursing in 1872. Morison (1960) reported that by 1893, the newly established American Society of Superintendents of Training Schools for Nurses (which later became the National League of Nursing Education in 1912) had begun to establish standards for nursing education. By 1917, there was a curriculum for educating student nurses, which served as the basic foundation for the many revisions needed to "keep up with the times and meet expectations" for the nursing curriculum of the future (263).

In her textbook, Morison (1960) listed the abilities that a nurse of the future may need, such as understanding the limitations of nursing practice, sharing nursing tasks with others, demonstrating skill in human relationships, identifying nursing problems, planning and providing nursing care that meets patient needs, performing nursing procedures skillfully, assuming responsibility for the promotion of health and prevention of disease, contributing to the welfare of the community, and behaving in accordance with a satisfying philosophy, which includes

3

goals of personal maturity and professional growth (267–270). Morison (1960) opted not to include writing skills in this projected list of critical nursing abilities, but she did offer some prescient, simple advice for nurses:

> Remember that as a graduate nurse, you may contribute to the public welfare by indicating a *willingness* to write. There is a definite need today for nurses who can write on topics related to their profession. You may excel in writing notices for newspapers concerning nursing activities. You may desire to write textbooks that will aid in education. Whatever type of writing you do, if you have the desire and ability, encourage both that nursing and health knowledge may be more widely disseminated to others (240).

Morison (1960) concluded that graduate nurses better society and contribute to the public welfare *by writing*, and she emphasized that, like all professions, nursing is obligated to develop standards of conduct, acquire knowledge and skills based on professional foundations, apply knowledge and skills that better society, and engage in continued study and research that advances the status and standards of the profession (67). At the core of professional obligation lies "the obligation to inform—to profess—that characterizes professionals," (Davis, 1991, 175). Morison (1960) said that the responsibility of a profession "entails continued study or research for advancement of status and standards," (67). Such advancement occurs through scholarship that generates both practice-oriented and theoretical knowledge within a discipline and professional publications. As Lambert and Lambert (2011) suggested ". . . It is through publications that nurses contribute to the greater good of the entire professional community" (80).

Professional Nursing Today

Fast forward almost sixty years, and the issue of writing skills in nursing ranks front and center as the nursing profession advances— sometimes smoothly and sometimes painfully—toward new, higher levels of skill and competence, new obligations, and new recognition of nursing's central role in the evolving, complex landscape of today's health care system in the era of the Patient Protection and Affordable Care Act (ACA). These advances have been propelled by a number of driving forces, such as, but not limited to, the Institute of Medicine (IOM) (2011). The IOM called for expanding the role for nurses and doubling the number of nurses with a doctorate by 2020, which sparked the birth of the following:

- New Doctor of Nursing Practice (DNP) programs
- A literal tsunami of new doctoral dissertations in nursing
- New regulations that enable advanced practice nurses (APNs) to establish standalone practices and a wider scope of practice (AAACN, 2010; Institute of Medicine, 2010; Johnson and Garvin, 2017; Yee, Boukus, Cross, and Samuel, 2013)
- The American Nurses Association (ANA), which in 2013 revised its competency model and reaffirmed that communication skills are key competencies for *all* registered nurses in *all* areas of practice, and that nurses must be able to write clearly, concisely, fluently, and eloquently about the many communications inherent in contemporary nursing practice
- The World Health Organization (WHO), which published a new competency model in 2016 that also identified communication skills as one of the key competencies for contemporary nurses

As we described in 2019 (Johnson and Rulo, 2019), many individual voices in the profession have echoed the critical importance of writing skills to the future of the nursing. In her introduction to the 2012 special issue of the *Journal of Nursing Administration*, entitled "The Art of Communicating Outcomes," Hill emphasized the critical importance of nurses' writing skills in communicating the value of nursing, the business case for resources and change, and the implementation of new nursing practices and processes based on evidence-based outcomes. In 2014, Oermann *et al.* said that the ability to communicate in writing allows nurses to participate fully in academic discourse; write about nursing practice in academic literature; fulfill the profession's obligation to disseminate research findings from evidence-based projects, innovations in clinical practice, and clinical research studies; and ultimately, to ensure the place of nurses as thought leaders in the health care system. In 2017, McQuerrey linked the critical importance of good writing skills to success as a nurse practitioner, in which great writing skills help to ensure the continuity of care and efficiency of information sharing with other health professionals. These and many other diverse voices have converged on a common theme: Writing in nursing is not optional—*nurses must be good writers*.

Given this reality, other authors have focused on the practical, painful, day-to-day challenges that nurses continue to experience as they struggle with the mechanics of writing. In 2002, one study of nursing students identified writing as one of the most difficult aspects of nursing education (Whitehead, 2002). In 2004, Harwood and Hartley suggested that the challenges of academic writing lie with the "bewildering set of rules, many of which are never made explicit to student writers" (156). Others added that some of nursing students' difficulty with writing could result from their limited experience with higher education, or, given the increasing diversity in nursing, from differences in their educational, cultural, or linguistic backgrounds (Borglin, 2011; Lea and Street, 2006; Whitehead, 2002). Borglin (2011) also suggested that certain characteristics of nursing education (more non-traditional students, young and antithetical sciences, the theory-practice divide, and more tutors and teachers who lack substantial teacher training) may present barriers to the development of writing proficiency, the acquisition of the "necessary basic knowledge in critical thinking," and ultimately the students' success in higher education (1). Borglin also said that nursing programs shoulder part of the blame because the typical academic content of the nursing curriculum focuses on acquiring clinical practice skills and often excludes content devoted to mastering communication, or techniques for appraising critical literature, so necessary for the implementation of evidenced-based practice.

Nursing Faculty Voice Concerns

In 2012, Cone and Van Dover cited research with nursing faculty who reported that writing continued to cause graduate students to experience significant distress and discouragement and that good candidates in the MSN program were dropping out of graduate school because of poor writing skills. Cone and Van Dover speculated that these students may never have received instruction or had forgotten how to write in formal prose, were not supported to write well, were fearful that they could not write well, or simply did not care enough to exert the considerable effort required by professional writing. Few graduate nursing programs require students to complete a writing course prior to or during their academic program. Although graduate school applications may require a writing sample, few nursing graduate students are asked to author a substantial research paper that includes a systematic literature review.

In addition, graduate students differ from younger, more traditional students who may study full time, because adult students experience challenges from multiple life commitments to work and family, as well as financial obligations (Gross and Clark, 2018). Within academic institutions today, writing deficiency is a significant issue (Lyons and

Elmedni, 2015). In one survey, graduate students reported that busy schedules prohibited revisions in their written work and that they did not expect faculty to request revisions (Seurkamp, 2007), despite the reality that experienced writers routinely spend literally half of their total writing time to revising draft documents (Scott, 2001).

Growth in University Writing Centers

In 2017, Ondrusek attributed the overall growth in university writing centers to the faculty's weak writing skills, causing an increased reliance in universities on external experts to fill this skill gap. In a recent publication about the conundrum about writing skills in nursing, Mitchell (2018) also focused on faculty skills as a major factor rarely acknowledged in nursing education or in the nursing literature. The nursing faculty may be unprepared to coach nursing students on writing pedagogy because writing instruction may have received little attention in their own graduate education, and the prototypical drilling exercises in basic writing skills have simply not engaged or helped student writers, Mitchell noted. According to Lea and Street (2006), to improve the writing skills of nurses, nursing educators must *demystify* academic writing for nursing students and also *show* them how to develop a variety of writing styles and genres and how to switch styles as needed for a variety of professional formats. This type of didactic instruction in writing is needed to help students increase their writing proficiency and broaden their portfolio of writing skills to include a number of literacy forms. Furthermore, the accrediting organizations in nursing expect the nursing faculty to equip students with writing skills that not only advance careers, but also the profession as well.

Irrespective of the diverse root causes, the reality is that poor writing skills pose a significant problem for today's nurses and the future of nursing profession (Johnson and Rulo, 2019). In today's health care environment, good writing is essential, not optional, because nurses exiting a graduate program need a broad portfolio of writing skills for their routine daily work. Consider these examples: An APRN or clinically based DNP-prepared nurse may be writing a business plan or developing an evidenced-based practice (EBP) project that must articulate crisp, cogent, and compelling arguments that can convince potential funders of the need for and viability of a new independent nursing enterprise or a major change in organizational practice. The reality is that a business plan or EBP project with many worthwhile ideas and poor writing has a slim chance of being funded. A graduate nursing student in a PhD program may be writing a research paper or policy brief required for a graduate class or a proposal for a doctoral dissertation that must meet very strict university or federal agency standards. A team of nurse clinicians may be collaborating on an article about an EBP to submit to a professional nursing journal, which has unique, exacting writing guidelines for authors. Additionally, a C-suite nurse executive may be serving as the lead author of an evaluation that assesses a new product under consideration for use in a complex healthcare system.

Core Writing Concepts

Across these different writing genres, nurses must use many core concepts of writing—voice, tone, style, audience analysis, framing, transitions, word choice, beginnings, and endings—as well as a host of different writing conventions and rules. Without understanding and applying these concepts, nurses risk writing with the deficiencies that typically face graduate students, such as lack of clarity, poor organization, weak construction of paragraphs, spelling and syntax errors, and poor document structure (Lea and Street, 2006), as well as weak transitions, difficulty changing writing style for different types of assignments, and incorrect or inconsistent use of the American Psychological Association (APA) style guidelines (2019), which must be followed for publication (Cone and Van Dover, 2012).

Identifying effective strategies for improving nurses' writing is complicated, according to Oermann *et al.* (2015), who assessed a wide range of approaches for improving writing, such as writing assignments, programs that integrate writing across the curriculum, online writing tutorials, use of a writing coach or a peer tutor, and writing workshops. Oermann *et al.*'s (2015) research team found evaluation studies of writing strategies to be very limited, and concluded that ". . . a paper assignment or writing activity in one course is not sufficient to build writing skills," instead, they suggested that ". . . a systematic plan is needed for the nursing program as a whole," (33).

At the systems level, a pragmatic plan to increase technical writing mastery in nursing must be based on a strong commitment by universities to competency in writing as a key professional competency. This involves elevating the importance of writing skills within and throughout the curriculum, improving the faculty's ability to teach students how to meet the expectations of excellence in writing for nursing papers and publications, providing significant faculty and student resources for training in writing, and expecting nursing students to enter graduate programs with baseline proficiency in scholarly writing.

As universities renew the focus on the importance of writing, individual nurses and faculty need assistance *now*—and that's where this practical guide to good writing in nursing comes in.

References

American Academy of Ambulatory Care Nursing (AAACN). 2010. *Ambulatory Care Nursing Administration and Practice Standards.* (8th ed.). Pitman, NJ: Author.

AACN (American Association of Colleges of Nursing). 2015. "The Doctor of Nursing Practice: Current Issues and Clarifying Recommendations." https://www.pncb.org/sites/default/files/2017-02/AACN_DNP_Recommendations.pdf.

American Nurses Association. 2013, August. Competency model. Washington, DC: The American Nurses Association. Retrieved from https://learn.ana-nursingknowledge.org/template/ana/publications_pdf/leadershipInstitute_competency_model-brochure.pdf

American Psychological Association. 2010. *Publication manual of the American Psychological Association.* (6th ed.). Washington, DC: American Psychological Association.

Borglin, G. 2012 "Promoting Critical Thinking and Academic Writing Skills in Nurse Education." *Nurse Education Today* 32, 611–613.

Cone, P. H. and L. Van Dover, L. 2012. "Shaping How Graduate Nursing Students Write." *Nursing Education Perspective* 33 (4), 272–273.

Davis, J. K. 1991. "Professions, trades and the obligation to inform." *Journal of Applied Psychology*, 8(2), 167–176. Retrieved from http://hssfaculty.fullerton.edu/philosophy/johndavis/documents/Davis-Professions,%20Trades,%20and%20the%20Obligation%20to%20Inform.pdf

Gross, N. and Clark, K. 2018. "Adult college students: The undercovered 6.6 million." Retrieved from https://www.ewa.org/blog-higher-ed-beat/adult-college-students-undercovered-66million

Harwood, N. and Hadley, G. 2002. "Demystifying institutional practices: Critical pragmatism and the teaching of academic writing." *English for Specific Purposes*, 23, 355–377.

Hill, K. S. 2012. The art of communicating outcomes. JONA, 42 (10), October Supplement. Johnson, J. and Garvin, W.S. (2017). "Advanced practice nurses: Developing a business plan for an independent ambulatory clinical practice." *Nursing Economics*, 35(3), 126–133, 141.

Institute of Medicine. 2011. *The Future of Nursing: Leading Change, Advancing Health* —Report recommendations. The National Academies Press, Washington, D.C. Retrieved from http://www.nationalacademies.org/hmd/~/media/Files/Report%20Files/2010/The-Future-of-Nursing/Nursing%20Education%202010%20Brief.pdf

Johnson, J. E. and Rulo, K. 2019. "Problem in the profession." *Journal of Professional Nursing, 35* (1), 57-64.

Lambert, V. A., and Lambert, C. E. 2011. "Why nurses don't publish." *Pacific Rim International Journal Of Nursing Research, 15*(2), 79-80.

Latham, C.L. and Ahern, N. 2013. "Professional writing in nursing education: Creating an Academic-community writing center." *Journal of Nursing Education, 33,* 615–620.

Lea, M.R. and Street, B.V. 2006. "The academic 'literacies model': Theory and application." *Theory into Practice, 45*(4), 368–377.

Lyons, B.P. and Ellmedni, B. 2015. "Writing skills development for graduate students: Workshop intervention using a student-centered learning approach." *Journal of Education and Social Policy, 2* (1), 38-49. Retrieved from http://jespnet.com/journals/Vol_2_No_1_March_2015/5.pdf

McQuerrey, L. 2017. "The importance of writing as a nurse practitioner." *Chron.* Retrieved from http://work.chron.com/importance-writing-nurse-practitioner-18156.html

Mitchell, K.M. 2018. "Constructing writing practices in nursing." *Journal of Nursing Education, 57*(7), 399–407.

Morison, L. J. 1960. *Steppingstones to professional nursing.* St. Louis. MO: The C.V Mosby Co.

Oermann, M.H., Leonardelli, A.K., Turner, K.M., Hawks, S.J., Derouin, A.L., and Hueckel, R.M. 2015. "Systematic review of educational programs and strategies for developing Students' and nurses' writing skills." *Journal of Nursing Education 54*(10), 28–34.

Ondrusek, A. L. 2017. "What the research reveals about graduate students' writing skills: A literature review." *Journal of Education for Library and Information Services, 53*(3), 176–188.

Seurkamp, M.P. 2007. "Changing student demographics." *University Business, 10*(10), 47–48.

Scott, J.C. (2001). Using the process approach to improve scholarly writing. *Delta Pi Epsilon Journal, 43,* 57–66.

Whitehead, D. 2002. "The academic writing experience of a group of nursing students: a phenomenological study." *Journal of Advanced Nursing, 38*(5), 498–505.

World Health Organization. 2016. "Nurse educator core competencies." Geneva, Switzerland: WHO. Retrieved from http://www.who.int/hrh/nursing_midwifery/nurse_educator050416.pdf?ua=1

Yee, T., Boukus, E.R., Cross, D. and Samuel, D.R. 2013, February. "Primary Care Workforce Shortages: Nurse Practitioner Scope-of-Practice Laws and Payment Policies. Research Brief No. 13." *National Institute of Health Care Reform.* Washington, DC. Retrieved from https://www.nihcr.org/analysis/improving-care-delivery/prevention-improving-health/pcp-workforce-nps/

CHAPTER 2

Acquiring and Enhancing Writing Skill Sets

*The mere fact that a course contains a focus on writing sets it
apart from most others in the typical graduate school curriculum.*
—Sallee, Hallett, and Tierney 2011

Introduction

ACADEMIC writing proficiency and the development of critical thinking and analytic skills hallmark graduate nursing education and are fundamental to successful program completion (Borglin 2012). Mastery of these skills underpins quality academic work, future professional engagement, and knowledge dissemination. Despite this, most nursing faculty acknowledge that many students leave graduate nursing programs better able to critique, analyze, and synthesize, but without substantial improvement in the technical writing skills that are so important to their professional futures.

To acknowledge the importance of the issue and address the root cause—poor secondary education—academic accrediting organizations in nursing expect graduate schools to equip students with writing skills that will advance the profession through postgraduate knowledge dissemination. This chapter reviews root causes for the substandard level of writing of many nurses enrolled in graduate degree programs, program accreditation expectations for graduate level writing proficiency, university-based programs that assist students in improving writing skills, relevant adult-learning principles, and writing expectations for advanced practice, DNP and PhD-prepared nurses, and other nurses.

A Failed Educational System

Poor writing in graduate school reflects weakness in undergraduate writing, as evidenced by a 2005 survey that found only 11% of college seniors to be proficient writers. (Abbate-Vaughn 2007). In a 2006 follow-up report from the Partnership for 21st-Century Skills, employers found that 26% of college students had deficient writing skills (Inc. 2016), whereas The Conference Board (2006) found that 25% of college graduates were poor writers. Inc. (2016) also found that only 50% of 2,300 college students believed that their writing skills improved during their four-year education.

Why are writing skill sets so weak? Who is to blame? The problem largely rests with secondary education (Tucker 2017). Today, high school students are rarely required to write anything of significant length because the traditional focus from basic grammar, sentence structure, word choice, and usage shifted to creative writing, which relaxed the emphasis on basic writing mechanics (Downey 2016; Tucker 2017). Results from a 2011 National Assessment of Educational Progress (NAEP) survey found that only 24% of twelfth-graders achieved or surpassed the proficient writing level and only 3% could write at an advanced level. The survey revealed problems that ranged from an abundance of sentence fragments, failure to recognize run-on sentences, and lack of subject-verb agreement to punctuation errors and misuse of words (NAEP 2011).

In an opinion editorial, a university English professor lamented "How in 15 short weeks can I possibly undo the harm that's been done by teachers who ignore the glaring writing and thinking faults I regularly encounter? And how can I possibly convince these students that my assessment of their writing is valid when their high school teachers led them to believe something very different? After all, they've got a diploma to prove it." (Downey 2016).

Reality shock. In general, students who are applying for college are not required to submit a long paper in which they present and justify a hypothesis, or analyze a complicated subject from differing viewpoints and arrive at a logical conclusion. Unfortunately, this is exactly what professors expect them to do and do well in college (Tucker 2017). For nurses, the problem is more complex because undergraduate nursing programs focus less on lengthy written assignments and more on technical proficiency in the basic sciences and knowledge transfer to clinical decision-making. In addition, nursing faculty typically focus their efforts on preparing undergraduate students to pass the Health Education Systems, Inc. (HESI) examinations and the National Council Licensure Examination (NCLEX) examination, which are required to enter the nursing profession and practice safely as a registered nurse. Most nurses who seek an advanced graduate degree have weak writing skills at a time when writing requirements in graduate programs challenge even the best writers (Cafferella and Barnett 2000; Cooper and Bikowski 2007; Harris 2006).

In 1989, Cheshire suggested that the typical writing-review-revision process contributes significantly to the uncomfortable shock experienced by most graduate students. The review and revision process takes time and requires uninterrupted concentration. Coupled with work commitments, family and financial obligations, significant stress can result because writing is an integral component in masters and doctoral education (Chao, DeRocco, and Flynn 2007). Contributing to the problem is that few graduate nursing programs require students to complete a writing course prior to or during their academic program. Fortunately, universities have created writing centers that help students improve writing skills.

University Writing Centers

On the campuses of many American colleges and universities today, writing centers offer guidance for students who are struggling with writing skills. Although these centers differ in name, personnel, teaching method, and funding, their presence and function significantly contributes to creating a supportive academic environment (Walker 2002). Writing centers began to take off in the late 1960s in response to a significant wave of college enrollments and flourished in the 1970s with the onset of open-admission policies that responded to affirmative action legislation (Boquet 1999; Yahner and Murdick 1991). Today, university-based writing centers are fundamental to student support services, because they assist students who are struggling with writing proficiency.

Despite the impressive growth of these writing services, the demand for student support may fall short, often because of unrealistic student expectations (Brooks 2001). In many cases, students expect to rely on a professional editor at their university writing center to transform a poorly written draft assignment into a well-written manuscript ready for submission. Instead, many students are surprised to find writing center personnel who critique draft manuscripts, suggest writing exercises for skill growth, and expect students to use the suggestions and revise their own work (Brooks 2001). As a result, dismayed students must revise, reformat, and edit documents to correct lack of clarity, logical flow, and grammatical errors.

Nevertheless, university writing centers have emerged as a mainstay of undergraduate and graduate student support and have moved from a marginal position on campus to a central university function staffed by personnel with graduate degrees and expertise in writing (Kinkead 2001). The enhanced writing instruction offered by these centers has enabled countless students to advance academically and achieve success. Most importantly, the knowledge and improved writing skills have equipped graduates to succeed in their careers and in the dissemination of knowledge through publication.

The Catholic University of America (2017) Writing Center suggests that students interested in accessing writing center services will find the following:

- Tutor availability with personalized one-on-one attention
- Faculty equipped to teach students practical skills in writing
- An environment that encourages discussion, collaboration, and the sharing of knowledge and ideas
- Availability of support that supports academic program requirements
- Online program access for distanced-learning students
- Peer tutoring that includes peer editing
- Collaboration between writing center faculty and academic program faculty

Nursing School Program(s) Accreditation Requirements

"Pity the poor nursing student, who is required to write at times like a sociologist, at others like a philosopher, yet again like a scientist and finally as a reflective practitioner!" (Baynham 2001, 188)

With writing considered one of the most important components of scholarship (Whitehead 2002), it makes sense that organizations that accredit nursing programs would reinforce the importance of technical writing in accreditation standards and include the demonstration of writing expertise as part of the approval process. The two major nursing program accrediting bodies, The American Association of Colleges of Nursing and The National League for Nursing, provide detailed requirements that nursing programs must meet to achieve and retain program accreditation. Are these requirements sufficiently detailed to advance writing proficiency in graduate programs? Consider the focus of both organizations.

The American Association of Colleges of Nursing (AACN)

The AACN provides the required content for graduate DNP nurses in its *The Essentials of Doctoral Education for Advanced Nursing Practice* (AACN 2006). The AACN defined the DNP degree as a "practice-focused" degree, which differentiated it from the PhD, or "research-focused" doctorate (AACN 2006, 3). The *Essentials* focus on the program-specific content required for accreditation, as illustrated in Table 2.1, and are considered "the foundational outcome competencies deemed essential" for all DNP program graduates (AACN 2006, 8).

TABLE 2.1. The Essentials of Doctoral Education for Advanced Nursing Practice.

I. *Scientific Underpinnings for Practice*—focuses on life processes, human behavior, optimal human functioning in health or illness, interaction with the environment, and nursing's role in creating positive change.
II. *Organizational & Systems Leadership for Quality Improvement and Systems Thinking*—focuses on the needs of the larger population, including the development of new care delivery models, that conflate with organizational, political, cultural, and economic perspectives.
III. *Clinical Scholarship and Analytical Methods for Evidence-Based Practice*—focuses on the translation of research into practice, including the dissemination and integration of new knowledge.
IV. *Information Systems/Technology (IT) and Patient Care Technology for the Improvement and Transformation of Health Care*—focuses on the ability to use IT to support and improve patient care, healthcare systems, and institutional leadership.
V. *Health Care Policy for Advocacy in Health Care*—focuses on policy development in all venues and political activism as a method to influence health policy and address subject areas such as health disparities, ethics, access to care, quality of care, financing, equity, and social justice.
VI. *Interprofessional Collaboration for Improving Patient and Population Health Outcomes*—focuses on membership in complex, multi-tiered healthcare teams working collaboratively and overcoming impediments to professional practice through the DNP's acquisition of leadership skills.
VII. *Clinical Prevention and Population Health for Improving the Nation's Health*—focuses on health promotion and risk /illness reduction for individuals, families, and the served community defined by gender, diagnosis, or age.
VIII. *Advanced Practice Nursing*—focuses on the development of increased specialized knowledge, advanced levels of clinical judgment and systems thinking that enables the assessment of complex health and illness parameters, and the design, implementation, and evaluation of interventions based on nursing and other sciences.

Source: American Association of Colleges of Nursing (AACN) 2006.

The intent of these eight essentials is to produce doctoral-level graduates who have advanced competencies, which require graduates to articulately communicate, justify, and argue for each component in the *Essentials*. The expectation is that graduates with advanced doctoral degrees will disseminate knowledge through professional publications, policy briefs, business cases, and innovative evidence-based projects. *Essential III—Clinical Scholarship and Analytical Methods for Evidence-Based Practice* addresses the expectation that expert writing skills will be an outcome of graduate level nursing education (AACN 2006). It is this *Essential* that effectively requires programs to focus on the translation of new science and the generation of evidence that will guide practice and outcome improvements, all of which will be disseminated through multiple avenues of communication, including scholarly publications.

The National League for Nursing (NLN)

In 2016, the NLN published new accreditation standards for all graduate and undergraduate nursing programs. Programs accredited by the NLN must meet five specific standards that are measured by quality indicators. The NLN has the authority to accredit all nursing programs: LPN/LVN, diploma, associate, bachelor's, master's, and clinical doctorate degrees. The NLN's global reach promotes integrity in nursing education and focuses on continuous quality improvement to prepare a skilled nursing workforce (Cannon and Halstead 2019). The five NLN standards, illustrated in Table 2.2, include interpretative guidelines for all nursing programs.

The NLN Standards modestly underscore the importance of expertise in knowledge dissemination or written communication. However, they emphasize data gathering and analysis in demonstrating program achievement, which suggests a greater focus on quality in information and data dissemination (Cannon and Halstead 2019; NLN 2016). Scholarship is emphasized in *Standards II and III*, and for faculty, is expanded in *Standards IV and V* for students: "Student support including tutoring . . . incorporates a foundation of arts into the program of study" (NLN, 2016).

Standard V emphasizes that doctoral programs must build on masters' program competencies that are specific to the practice role. This standard focuses on the role of faculty in designing new and revising existing curricula based on the evidentiary needs of the profession.

TABLE 2.2. NLN Commission for Nursing Education Accreditation
Standards for Nursing Education Programs.

I. *Culture of Integrity and Accountability: Mission, Governance and Resources*—focuses on program governance, mission, goals, core values, and envisioned outcomes; emphasizes a culture of integrity and accountability
II. *Culture of Excellence and Caring: Faculty*—focuses on faculty expertise, innovation and creativity, and the organizational environment that enables faculty to thrive in achieving expected professional outcomes.
III. *Culture of Excellence and Caring: Students*—student-center support services and a learning environment beginning with student recruitment and admission to graduation; evidence of a caring environment that fosters student success.
IV. *Culture of Learning and Diversity: Curriculum and Teaching/Learning/Evaluation Processes*—focuses on accommodating the needs of diverse learners in the teaching, learning and evaluation processes; distance-learners are held to the same standard as on-campus students.
V. *Culture of Excellence: Program Outcomes*—program modifications based on assessment, evaluation, and data with a commitment to continuous quality improvement.

Source: National League for Nursing 2016.

Since knowledge dissemination easily conforms with advancement of the profession, the NLN steadfastly supports the role of faculty in equipping graduate nursing students with solid technical writing skills (NLN 2016, 27). Furthermore, the NLN offers dedicated resources that enhance faculty writing proficiency through a robust continuing education program focused on faculty writing proficiency. One example is the *NLN Scholarly Writing Retreat* that for more than ten years has assisted nurse educators in elevating their writing skills, publishing scholarly work, and disseminating research findings (NLN 2019).

Writing Considerations

For Students in Graduate Nursing Programs

As Sallee, Hallett, and Tierney (2011) suggest, ". . . The mere fact that a course contained a focus on writing sets it apart from most others in the typical graduate school curriculum" (66). Student manuscripts generally vary in quality—some students submit polished manuscripts, whereas others submit work with poor sentence structure, typographical errors, and errors in grammar and syntax. Even the best writers, however, can benefit from practice and remedial exercises (Sallee, Hallett and Tierney 2011).

All strategies that support graduate nursing students in their focus on achieving better writing skills must take into consideration key learner characteristics of adult students, such as self-directedness, intrinsic motivation, and application of personal and professional knowledge to achieve desired outcomes (Ross-Gordon 2011). As adult learners, graduate students focus their learning on problems or challenges identified by course professors. Feedback from professors activates the internal motivation in adult learners to address deficits. Therefore, graduate students should expect and welcome feedback and advice from professors on their writing abilities.

Applying adult learning theory to improving writing proficiency also suggests that adult learners may be more likely to improve writing habits if they can utilize new writing skills immediately after instruction *and* receive persuasive feedback for engaging in newly developed writing skills. Because repetitive practice changes attitudes toward new tasks, the more adult learners engage in practicing new writing skills, the less likely they are to return to former old habits (Ondrusek 2017).

Students should determine the commitment of their university and nursing program to their personal mastery of scholarly writing. Students who fully engage in elevating their writing skill should expect to achieve significant improvement in their writing by the end of their academic experience. Graduate nursing students may find that focusing on four key topics is helpful in improving writing.

First, understand that *technical writing ability* encompasses writing mechanics that include, but are not limited, to adherence to specific formatting requirements (such as the APA, MLA), understanding of plagiarism, and skills in proofreading that can eliminate errors.

Second, aim to convey content *clearly, concisely, and logically* by expressing content without weak sentence structure, weak verbs, or passive voice *and* with logical flow or sequencing, correct writing rubrics, and the demonstration of higher order thinking skills in critical analysis, evaluation, and synthesis.

Third, invite professor perspectives on your academic writing and use that feedback to improve your writing skills. Students in the academic setting should answer these questions: Are course assignments expected to demonstrate the higher order thinking skills of analysis, synthesis, and evaluation? Are writing performance expectations contained in assignment rubrics? Are points deducted for course work with poor technical writing skills? How invested is my professor in critiquing to improve my writing proficiency?

Fourth, assess university commitment to strengthening student writing proficiency via established standards for writing. Are guidelines/expectations clearly articulated? Is writing mastery an expectation threaded through all courses with the same level of interest and intensity? Has the university or program developed any lectures or courses that specifically address technical writing expectations at the graduate program level? The answers to these questions can help graduate students determine university and program commitment to improving writing.

For Nursing APRNs, DNPs, and PhDs in Professional Roles

Within the protective world of university life where learning is central, graduate students can improve their writing deficits with focus and hard work. However, after graduation, workplace settings expect writing to be honed and conducive to advancing the organization and its workforce (Sallee, Hallett, and Tierney 2011). In fact, many employers require evidence of solid writing as part of the employment process (Inc. 2016), which is a significant difference from the traditional importance of technical skills in nursing.

As a nurse leader in the many diverse roles available today, leaders who can effectively communicate in writing enjoy the advantages of leadership support. This applies to documents required for developing new and innovative clinical programs, crafting evidence-based practice projects that improve clinical outcomes, or drafting policy briefs that underscore health promotion and risk reduction in the diverse communities served by nurses with advanced degrees.

In the work of clinically based DNP nurses or a PhD nurse in the C-Suite, executives extend little forgiveness for poorly constructed documents. The ability of clinical nurses and nurse leaders to write well is one important measure of the elite professional nurse with a Masters, DNP, or PhD degree. These nurse leaders can benefit from writing workshops, bootcamps, and retreats designed to elevate writing skills through full immersion with uninterrupted time for learning, writing exercises, and the practicing new skills and techniques. Some of these programs include the NLN's Scholarly Writing Retreat, the Scholars Voice Weekend Writing Workshop, and the Gotham Writers Workshop. Local and online universities also offer a myriad of writing courses.

Acquiring and enhancing one's writing skills requires a commitment to learn new techniques and then practice, practice, practice. This chapter discussed the challenges of higher education in developing competent writers, the writing challenges of many nursing students, and the contribution of university-based writing centers to improving writing skills. The brief review of nursing accreditation programs reinforced that nursing programs must prepare students for successful knowledge dissemination upon graduation. Finally, adult learning principles apply both to nursing graduate students and practicing clinicians who are responsible for programmatic, policy, and business case development.

References

AACN (American Association of Colleges of Nursing). 2006. *The Essentials of Doctoral Education for Advanced Nursing Practice*. https://www.aacnnursing.org/DNP/DNP-Essentials.

Abbate-Vaughn, J. 2007. "The Graduate Writing Challenge: A Perspective From an Urban Teacher Education Program." *Action in Teacher Education* 29 (2), 51–60. https://doi.org/10.1080/01626620.2007.10463448.

Baynham, M. 2002. "Academic Writing in New and Emerging Discipline Areas." In *Perspectives on Learning*. Vol 1, edited by R. Harrison, F. Reeve, A. Hanson, and J. Clarke. London: Rutledge Falmer.

Borglin, G. 2012. "Promoting Critical Thinking and Academic Writing Skills in Nurse Education." *Nurse Education Today* 32 (5), 611–613. https://doi.org/10.1016/j.nedt.2011.06.009.

Boquet, E. 1999. "'Our little secret': A history of writing centers, pre- to post-open admissions." *College Composition and Communication, 50*(3), 463–482. Retrieved from https://www.jstor.org/stable/358861

Brooks, J. 2001. "Minimalist tutoring: making the student do all the work." In R.W. Barnett and J.S. Blummer (Eds.) *The Allyn and Bacon Guide to Writing Center Theory and Practice*. (219). Boston, MA, USA: Allyn and Bacon.

Caffarella, R.S. and Barnett, B.G. 2000. "Teaching doctoral students to become scholarly writers: The importance of giving and receiving critiques." *Studies in Higher Education, 25*(1), 39–52. Retrieved from https://doi.org/10.1080/030750700116000

Cannon, S. and Halstead, J. 2019. "Applying the NLN CNEA Standards to Your Program." Retrieved from http://www.nln.org/docs/default-source/accreditation-services/concurrent-session-handouts.pdf?sfvrsn=10

Chao E., DeRocco, E., and Flynn, M. 2007. *Adult learners in higher education: Barriers to success and strategies to improve results*. Washington, DC: U.S. Department of Labor, Employment and Training Administration, Office of Policy Development Research.

Cheshire, B.W. 1989. "Graduate student writing assistance in the counseling center." *Journal of College Student Development, 30*, 164-165.

Cooper A., and Bikowski, D. 2007. "Writing at the graduate level: What tasks do professors actually require?" *Journal of English for Academic Purposes*, 6(3), 206–221. Retrieved from https://doi.org/10.1016/j.jeap.2007.09.008

Downey, M. 2016, December 7. "Opinion: Students today are misled by fake news and fake grades." Retrieved from https://www.ajc.com/blog/get-schooled/opinion-students-today-are-misled-fake-news-and-fake-grades/oW9NqJrFwlVCt8R4Xl-w0KP/

Harris, M.J. 2006. "Three steps to teaching abstract and critique writing." *International Journal of Teaching and Learning in Higher Education*, *17*(2), 136-146. Retrieved from https://pdfs.semanticscholar.org/339b/2b26eda7072bac43452f0896660afdd45bca.pdf?_ga=2.48124448.623418602.1568829496-1214085208.1567025855

Kinkead, J. 2001. "The National Writing Centers Association as mooring: A personal history of the first decade." In R.W. Barnett, and J.S. Blummer (eds.). *The Allyn and Bacon Guide to Writing Center Theory and Practice*, (29–40). Boston, MS, USA: Allyn and Bacon.

Moore, K. 2016. "Study: Poor Writing Skills Are Costing Businesses Billions." Retrieved from https://www.inc.com/kaleigh-moore/study-poor-writing-skills-are-costing-businesses-billions.html

National Assessment of Educational Progress (NAEP). 2011. Department of Education:

National Center for Education Statistics. Retrieved from https://catalog.data.gov/dataset/2011-national-assessment-of-educational-progress

National League for Nursing. 2016. "Accreditation Standards for Nursing Education Programs." http://www.nln.org/docs/default-source/accreditation-services/cnea-standards-final-february-201613f2bf5c78366c709642ff00005f0421.pdf?sfvrsn=12.

National League for Nursing. 2019. "The NLN Scholarly Writing Retreat." Retrieved from http://www.nln.org/centers-for-nursing-education/nln-chamberlain-university-college-of-nursing-center-for-the-advancement-of-the-science-of-nursing-education2/scholarly-writing-retreat

Ondrusek, A.L. 2012. "What the research reveals about graduate students' writing skills: A literature review." *Journal of Education for Library and Information Services*, *53*(3), 176–188.Retrieved from https://www.jstor.org/stable/23249110

Ross-Gordon, J. M. 2011. "Research on adult learners: Supporting the needs of a student population that is no longer traditional." *Association for American Colleges and Universities*. *3*(1), 1. Retrieved from https://www.aacu.org/publications-research/periodicals/research-adult-learners-supporting-needs-student-population-no

Sallee, M., Hallett, R., and Tierney, W. 2011. "Teaching writing in graduate school." *College Teaching, 59* (2), 66–72. Retrieved from https://doi.org/10.1080/87567555.2010.511315

The Conference Board 2006. "Most young people entering the U.S. workforce lack critical skills essential for success." Retrieved from http://www.p21.org/news-events/press-releases/250-most-young-people-entering-the-us-workforce-lack-critical-skills-essential-for-success

The Catholic University of America. 2017. "The CUA Writing Center." Retrieved from http://english.cua.edu/wc/

Tucker, M. 2017, January 12. "Our students can't write very well—it's no mystery why." Retrieved from http://blogs.edweek.org/edweek/top_performers/2017/01/our_students_cant_write_very_wellits_no_mystery_why.html

Walker, S. C. 2002. "A brief history of university writing centers: Variety and diversity" Retrieved from https://www.newfoundations.com/History/WritingCtr.html

Whitehead, D. 2002. "The academic writing experience of a group of nursing students: A phenomenological study." *Journal of Advanced Nursing, 38*(5), 498–506. Retrieved from https://doi.org/10.1046/j.1365-2648.2002.02211.x

Yahner W., and Murdick W. 1991. "The evolution of a writing center: 1972–1990." *The Writing Center Journal, 11*(2), 16.

SECTION II

CHAPTER 3

A Rhetoric for Nursing Writers

Wherever there is persuasion, there is rhetoric.
And wherever there is "meaning," there is "persuasion."
—Kenneth Burke

Introduction

THE medieval philosopher Thomas Aquinas (1252-56/1997) once quoted Aristotle on reasoning to the effect that a "small error at the outset can lead to great errors in the final conclusions." So it is with writing. Behind all attempts to improve as a writer lies an implied understanding about what good writing is. If this implicit understanding is flawed, even only partially, your efforts to improve will be hampered and could lead to seriously defective results. Thus, the importance of the question, "What is good writing?" Perhaps you answer that good writing is writing that is free of mistakes. Or good writing flows well. Or good writing communicates clearly. These are all fine answers as they go—and certainly these qualities are inherent in much if not all writing that can be called "good"—but we would suggest that to define good writing adequately would require a broader lens. This broader lens rests the definition of good writing on the principle of rhetorical effectiveness. Good writing is whatever is rhetorically effective. And just what is rhetoric? The theorist Kenneth Burke (1950) defines rhetoric as the "use of words by human agents to form attitudes or to induce actions in other human agents" (41). In this way, rhetorical effectiveness would constitute those language acts that result in effects upon others as the agent of such acts intends. I am trying to persuade you of the public health crisis that could ensue if certain vaccination guidelines are not followed. I can call my communication rhetorically effective if you are so persuaded. All of our communications are goal oriented, and rhetorical effectiveness concerns the meeting of our communicative goals. But there is more. Rhetoric—and by extension rhetorical effectiveness—also implies the careful analysis of the rhetorical choices available to me and the analysis of rhetorical acts more generally. This dimension of rhetoric Aristotle (4th Century B.C.E/1926) aptly defines as the "faculty of discovering the possible means of persuasion in reference to any subject whatever" (15). To persuade you to adopt the vaccination guidelines, I have to know a great deal about the situation in which I am communicating, about you and your values, your level of knowledge of the subject, in addition to and entirely apart from my disciplinary expertise in the research on vaccinations and public health. In other words, I must consider situations, audience, and purpose and tailor my message to those factors in order to communicate successfully. Good writing, therefore, cannot be reduced merely to certain objective qualities like clarity, coherence, or correctness, because effective communication is ultimately dependent upon a much wider complex of factors. To assess whether or not a particular piece of prose is "good," we need to know a great deal about the context and situation: the when and where, to whom the writing was addressed, the unique needs and disposition of the addressee, the venue and genre, the reason for communicating.

So, what is good writing? The only sensible answer is, it depends. If you are tasked with writing a book review, it is best to not write a polemical tract. If it turns out that your audience for your proposal to adopt the vaccination guidelines is largely hostile, you may decide that it is best to begin first by addressing counterarguments rather than by launching into your proposals. If you write rap lyrics in your spare time, you probably would want to ditch the rules of standard English grammar for these songs. Even correctness is context-dependent. Don't misunderstand: Surely a mastery of language and technical facility are important, and we will study these in detail in the coming chapters. However, ultimately what good writing demands is nothing short of *a rhetorical way of thinking*: a habit and method of mind that analyzes the elements of communicative acts and makes informed choices about what will be effective in the given situation that the writer faces. This way of thinking, while more analytic than the mere perfection of skill, is not strictly speaking like the disciplinary methods of thought that you develop in your nursing theory and practice. An education in rhetoric is not an education into another specialty. As Steven Mailloux (2017) has suggested, rhetoric is not a discipline as we typically understand the term; it is more properly termed an "interdiscipline" that operates through disciplinairities to facilitate "critical work in various intellectu-al spaces" (2). Developing your rhetorical thinking will aid your ability to communicate effectively as a nursing researcher and leader and will be thereby a great boon to the professional work that you do, including in the higher impact areas of the dissemination of your research and in matters of public and administrative policy. Nursing as a field needs a leadership of effective and persuasive communicators and this requires a mastery of the interdiscipline of rhetoric.

The present chapter will provide you with the needed grounding in rhetorical principles to help you analyze and effectively communicate in any writing situation. You can't always have a writing expert on hand to help you through the composition process, but if you master the con-cepts found in this chapter, you will be able to make well-informed decisions about the rhetorical choices you face. The chapter is struc-tured around the points of Aristotle's centuries-old formulation of the rhetorical triangle (see Figure 3.1). The triangle represents the basic dimensions and dynamics of every significant communicative act. As it shows, each act of communication includes an author or agent. Each message centers on a subject and is addressed to a particular readership or audience (one or more). The verbal act is motivated by a purpose or rhetorical intention (the agent has a goal in mind that the communica-tion should achieve) and occurs within a broader context that includes the genre and situation of the writing. This simple visual representation yields a rich framework for structuring your communications for opti-mal effectiveness. We will deal with each aspect of the triangle in turn.

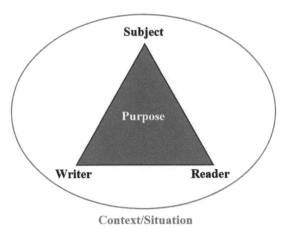

Figure 3.1. *The Rhetorical Triangle.*

Reader (Audience)

If good writing can be defined, as we have said, as communication that exhibits a strategic awareness of audience and tailors the message to the intended audience, then it follows that all writing, by the fact of its being written, is written *for someone*: the reader is implied, or should be, in the writing. What does this mean for you in your writing? At the most basic level, it means that being aware of your audience—that is, understanding and analyzing certain important characteristics shared by your readers or by large segments of your readers—can help you to make informed decisions about your writing. Figure 3.2 outlines the basic components of audience analysis.

One of the more important distinctions for you as a graduate student and/or professional nursing writer is to determine whether your audience is academic or general. If your audience is academic, you can assume a different level of background information for your reader, which may require less explanation or in some cases no explanation at all; you can expect to use more technical terminology where appropriate and you can be more confident that these terms will be understood. Given their aims and objectives, academic readers also generally tend to invest more time into texts that they encounter as research. You can expect, in other words, longer reading times and more careful, discriminating readers. You should also expect that, while your academic audience knows quite a bit about your topic, they will be much more interested than a more general or popular audience in hearing from you about how your research fits into a larger conversation that is on-going—in other words, the academic audience has an interest, which the non-academic audience lacks, in your research as a contribution; the academic audience wants to know how your research is new, in what ways it differs from what we've known on the topic, why it matters (answering the "so what?" question).

Audience	Level of Expertise	Reading Time	Contribution of Research
Academic	High	More	Important
Professional	High	Less	Important
General	Low	Less	Not important

Figure 3.2. Audience Analysis.

Nursing as a field of practice also includes a third category of audience that is neither general nor academic, strictly speaking: the professional audience. You encounter this audience as you present your research and findings to practitioners in the field or other professionals, such as executives with decision-making power. Such audiences may not have the same level of expertise as do professors and graduate students, but they certainly have practical expertise and are much more familiar with backgrounds, contexts, and terminologies than a general audience would be. In the case of communicating to this kind of audience, you would need ask yourself as you draft and revise how the information that you are presenting would be interpreted and understood by the addressee. Does your audience know your key terms? Do they have an understanding of the relevance of the problem, why it matters? How much background knowledge do they have? Do they have a particular stake or interest in the history of the literature? Answering these questions before and during the drafting process will help you shape your communications for optimal effectiveness.

Although the distinction between academic, general, and professional audiences or readerships is a helpful and necessary one to make, there are further nuances that must be taken into account. For example, you may find yourself presenting your research in a free clinic in a lower income community or at a community center in a high income neighborhood. Both of these audiences are general, that they lack disciplinary expertise about your subject (they are neither scholars, students, practitioners, nor administrators). Although the audiences may be general, they are very different nonetheless, and your presentations to each of them would need to be quite different to be effective. The same could be said for academic audiences. Writing to your professor would certainly count as an academic audience, but it makes a great deal of difference if you are writing to your professor as the instructor of your seminar versus as the director of your dissertation. One important difference is that the knowledge gap between author and reader is most likely going to be wider in the case of the seminar (the reader/professor has more knowledge of your topic and research than you do), whereas that gap will probably be lesser in the case of a dissertation (indeed, by the end of the doctoral process, you are likely to be just as expert on your topic, if not necessarily as expert in the art of research, as your professor). Similarly, the journal article reader assumes that you, the publishing author, are the expert, whereas a seminar paper author or even a dissertator does not have that same benefit of the doubt and is expected to demonstrate as explicitly as possible and to a much greater extent expertise and knowledge on the topic (mainly through more extensive referencing and discussion of background and methodological material). (For more on these dynamics in relation to credibility and authority, see the later section in this chapter.)

Purpose

Closely related to questions of audience are those of purpose. Every piece of writing is shaped by its author's purpose, otherwise known as rhetorical intention, which is based in the writing's situation and context, that is, what it is trying to accomplish. To change someone's mind on an issue, explore a topic more deeply, invent material for the paper you have to write for tomorrow's class, or contribute to a discussion—the possible intentions for any piece of writing are many. Understanding intention to be rhetorical in nature foregrounds how your purpose conditions and shapes your message. This might sound abstract, but considering your purpose is vital to your success as a writer, especially in situations in which you are trying to grapple with new material and negotiate the various voices and positions of the research you are absorbing. Under these circumstances, it is easy for even the best of writers to lose sight of the bigger picture and produce writing that is muddled and vague. Much writing that fails at the graduate level does so because its purpose is not clear to the writer, reader, or both. If your intent as a writer is not clear to you, there is almost no chance that it will be clear to your reader. But, importantly, *just because* it is clear to you *does not mean* that it will necessarily be clear to your reader. Making sure you are clear about your purpose from the beginning, and that you renew your sense of your purpose as you draft and revise, is critical to producing orderly, well structured, and clear writing. Figure 3.3 lists common rhetorical intentions or purposes that you will have as an academic writer. You may be tasked with informing or summarizing other research or practices. Your purpose may be to analyze data or various approaches to a problem. You may be arguing for a particular position and thus trying to persuade others to hold that same position or to take the action that you think should be taken. You may be presenting new research that changes our understanding of the field in significant ways.

It is important to note that these various intents or purposes rarely exist except in some combination. Often our arguments must include moments in which we inform the reader of background information to

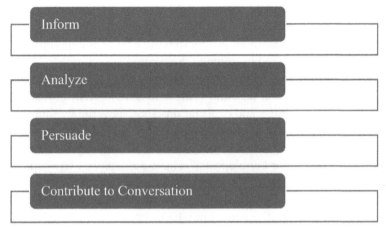

Figure 3.3. Rhetorical Intentions.

show how our argument relates to previous understanding. Or we need to offer extended analyses of collected data in service toward the larger argument that we are making. But even if there is rarely a simplified intent, it is important to ask: Which is the dominant purpose of my paper? What exactly am I trying to do? Inform an audience (or perhaps demonstrate competency to an instructor through informational summary)? Make an argument? Analyze a case study using a course concept? Explore my own thinking on a topic and how it relates to my personal practice experience? Each of these ends or purposes requires very different kinds of writing, and a bad decision in the beginning about your end will surely lead to a bad result.

Subject/Message

We have been considering the audience and purpose of your message, but what about the message itself? Under this heading, we would like to consider the question of genre. We aren't thinking of cowboy movies or romance novels but instead of the conventions and prior practices that shape communication. Writing studies theorist Charles Bazerman (2013) once said that genres are "ways of doing things" (24). Although we might tend to think of genres as relatively unimportant or even invisible in our acts of composition, Bazerman (1997) argues that genres "shape the thoughts we form and the communications by which we interact. "Genres" he continues, "are the familiar places we go to to create intelligible communicative action with each other and the guide-posts we use to explore the unfamiliar" (Bazerman 1997, 19). You as a writer will be never be asked simply to write a formless mass of words. You will never be asked to reinvent the writing wheel, either. You will always be writing in a genre that you did not create, that your professor or editor did not create, and that genre will have—as all genres do by definition—certain rules and expectations about how the writing should be carried out and about what it should look like. Exploring a topic through a particular genre will necessitate conforming your thought to that genre's particular "guideposts." These guideposts will shape your thought and will also allow you, as you gain more familiarity with the genre, to access the unfamiliarity of new information through the solid grounding of the familiar genres in which you encounter that informa-tion and in which you write. Awareness of genre helps to facilitate the process of acclimation to new genres. It also helps to shape your re-search and writing process, narrowing the boundaries of possible struc-tures and organizations for your research.

Most of the genres that you will write in as a nursing student and professional are what could be called "domesticated" genres, in that they do not exist out in the "wild" of the non-classroom world (Pri-or 1998; Soliday 2011, 13). You won't stumble upon any literature reviews as you browse the magazine rack at the grocery store, nor will you find a dissertation at your local bookstore. The genres of the graduate nursing student are those that you are likely to encounter only in the academic or professional setting. This can make writing in such genres especially difficult, because most often our apprehension of new writing forms occurs by intuition and by reading. Most of the sentences that we construct are variations and improvisations on sen-tences and on combinations of phrases and locutions that we have heard or read somewhere. We learn to write through the models of our read-ing, but because we have less exposure to the "domesticated" genres of the classroom, gaining facility with these forms can be a more arduous process.

Current research has shown that intentional learning about genres, and careful and conscious reading and emulation of models, can help facilitate transfer of genre writing knowledge (Bazerman 2005). With that mind, we will discuss briefly each of the major genres that you will encounter as a graduate nursing student and key characteristics for navigating those forms. A much more detailed treatment of the more familiar genres will be given in the following chapter.

Literature Reviews

The literature review can be divided into several discrete forms with different expectations and conventions. These differ by discipline (social sciences versus formal sciences) and by purpose (narrative versus systematic versus focused) (Feak and Swales 2009). Literature reviews present the existing body of knowledge about a topic, often including a history of the problem and how it has been treated as well as an outlining of work still needed to be done.

Dissertations

The dissertation is the longest document, usually a few hundred pages, that culminates a doctoral candidate's work toward completion of degree. It contributes new research to its field. In the social sciences and in the field of nursing, dissertations typically follow a standard chapter format, including an introduction, a literature review, methods, results, and a discussion (followed by references and appendices), although new novel models continue to emerge.

Seminar Papers

Seminar papers are longer research-oriented papers due often at the end of a semester-long graduate course. They can have various rhetorical intents. For example, you may be asked to research and demonstrate mastery of a theory or methodology, conduct a policy analysis, and/or provide reports of research conducted.

Journal Articles

You will gain familiarity with journal articles from doing research in your classes. Seminar papers can sometimes resemble journal articles in that they are both longer, self-contained documents of roughly similar length. Beware, though, that there are important differences between articles and seminar papers. Journal articles are written for a wider audience beyond the specific seminar class, so they need to do much more work to articulate rationale and purpose. This will often mean that more context needs to be provided and more work needs to be done to show how the research contributes to the existing body of knowledge.

Reflection and Narrative Writings

These types of writing can include narratives, journals, and other kinds of reflection or response writing. The purpose of these assignments can be to track your relationship to the material and to provide opportunities for you to explore your own thinking about course concepts and what you are learning. These can sometimes be difficult genres to navigate, because they also appear in the "wild" of the non-academic world in the form of journals or blogs. Be sure to pay attention to your instructor's guidelines and expectations for these assignments. If not presented, feel free to ask for clarification.

Writer (Author)

Writing for an audience not only requires that you scrutinize your readership and the genres in which you will be writing, but also demands that you consider carefully how you relate to your readership. The concept or *ethos* can be a helpful lens for thinking about that relationship. Rhetorical theory has considered ethos first within the context of speechmaking. Ethos in this setting can be defined as an appeal to the credibility of the speaker through the speech itself. Such an appeal can occur in a variety of ways: When a speaker makes a joke to bond with her audience or when she appeals to her own authority by alluding to her past experiences dealing with the topic being discussed. Appeals to ethos can also be made through the whole of the speech in the way that the audience has the impression by the totality of what is said that the speaker knows what she is talking about. While originating from analysis of the art of speechmaking, the concept of ethos is equally relevant for you as a writer.

The dynamics of ethos depend upon the relationship of the author and audience. Credibility is not something that is communicated in a vacuum. If an authority gap exists between author and audience, for example, this will affect how you might appeal to ethos (see Figure 3.4).

As a graduate student writing seminar papers mainly to your professor, the authority gap will be greater than that which exists between a dissertator and his director. Authority gaps can also exist between scholars but generally are less significant among peers. What is the rhetorical significance of an authority gap? Most importantly, for students, the act of communicating research to faculty concerns to a greater extent the need to demonstrate competency (see Figure 3.5). You are still learning

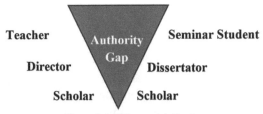

Teacher	Authority Gap	Seminar Student
Director		Dissertator
Scholar		Scholar

Figure 3.4. *Ethos and Authority.*

how to be a researcher and with your research *you are substantiating that you are in fact a researcher*. This is partly why it is so important at this stage to demonstrate competency in the basics of your field (e.g., grammatical correctness, clarity, knowledge of APA style, sound research methods, mastery of subject matter). For advanced researchers and faculty peers, the need to demonstrate competency is not absent by any means but it generally takes a backseat to teaching and disseminating (we come to their research to evaluate it but also and much more to learn from and be enriched by it). Young researchers must recognize that they do not write from positions of authority and, therefore, much of what they do in terms of their writing and research will in part have to do with establishing their authority and competency. In practice, this will entail making sure that you pay great attention to the details of your research, that you present polished materials, and that you work diligently to show your vast knowledge of the secondary literature, mastery of the methodology, and careful reasoning in your conclusions.

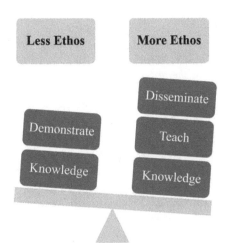

Figure 3.5. *Ethos and Writing.*

Practice Exercises

1. Select two of your previous writings and analyze them at length using the concepts introduced in this chapter. What was your purpose and do you think you achieved your rhetorical goals? How did you tailor your writing to your audience? In what ways was the writing shaped by the genre in which you were writing? How did you appeal to your ethos as a writer? Where do you think you could have been more rhetorically effective?

2. Select a recently published journal article and analyze its rhetoric using the concepts introduced in this chapter, answering the list of questions in Activity 1.

3. Pick a recent topic that you've researched or one that you would like to. Now consider how you would need to present that research differently in a scholarly journal article versus a talk to the general public. Draw up an outline for each paper, with a summary of the differences in approach.

References

Aristotle. 1926. *The "art" of rhetoric*. (J.H. Freese, Trans.) Cambridge, MA: Harvard University Press. (Original work published 4th Century B.C.E).

Bazerman, C. 2013. *A rhetoric of literature action: Literate action, volume 1*. Anderson, South Carolina: Parlor Press.

Bazerman, C. (2005). Genre and cognitive development: Beyond writing to learn. In C. Bazerman, A. Bonini, & D. Figueiredo (Eds.), *Genre in a changing world*. 279–94). Fort Collins, CO: Parlor Press.

Bazerman, C. 1997. The life of genre, the life in the classroom. 19-25. *Genre and writing: Issues, arguments, alternatives*. Portsmouth, NH: Heinemann.

Thomas Aquinas. 1997 *Medieval Sourcebook: Thomas Aquinas: On Being and Essence (DEENTE Et ESSENTIA)*. Translation by Robert T. Miller. Original published 1252–56. Retrieved from https://sourcebooks.fordham.edu/basis/aquinas-esse.asp

Burke, K. 1950. *A Rhetoric of Motives*. University of California Press: Berkeley.

Mailloux, S. 2017. *Rhetoric's pragmatism: Essays in rhetorical hermeneutics*. University Park, PA: The Pennsylvania State University Press.

Feak, C. B. & Swales, J.M. 2009. *Telling a research story: Writing a literature review*. Ann Arbor: University of Michigan Press.

Prior, P. 1998. *Writing/Disciplinarity: A sociohistoric account of literature activity in the academy*. New York: Routledge.

Soliday, M. 2011. *Everyday genres: Writing assignments across the disciplines*. Southern Illinois University Press: Carbondale, Ill.

Academic Writing at the Apex: The Masters Capstone Project Paper, The DNP EBP Project Scholarly Paper, and the PhD Dissertation

The only writer to whom you should compare yourself
is the writer you were yesterday.
—David Schlosser

Introduction

A S more nurses work toward advanced nursing degrees, confusion may exist about the writing requirements for the three different genres of academic writing that mark the culmination of different milestones in nursing education. In this chapter, we discuss each of the three genres, the commonalities among them, and some of the critical writing rules that help to ensure high quality writing.

The Capstone Project Paper

Capstone, defined by the *American Heritage Dictionary of the English Language* (2016) as a *crowning achievement,* is an apt title for the mandatory immersion courses that signal the end of a nurses' formal master's level graduate education and transition into advanced nursing practice. According to Martin, Brewer, and Barr (2011), capstone projects have become "the standard as a mechanism to prepare senior nursing students to enter the workforce" (1). These learning experiences are supervised by qualified faculty knowledgeable about developing evidence-based practice (EBP) projects. Although project implementation is traditionally not part of the master's program capstone experience, student must address all relevant project aspects with the intention to implement the innovation. The experience provides the soon-to-be masters-prepared nurse with a practical application of knowledge intended to improve clinical outcomes.

The final project report of the capstone course should demonstrate the student's analytic ability and proficiency in applying empirical evidence to solving a particular problem in nursing. The format can vary from a twenty-five page report to a presentation before a panel of experts, or a combination of the two. Students traditionally use the Population Intervention Comparison Outcomes (PICO) format, excluding the T or timeframe, because the proposed project is not intended for implementation at the master's level. Further, and in contrast to DNP EBP papers and doctoral dissertations that usually follow a very structured, traditional format, the written end-product of a capstone course can take very different forms such as a case study, a policy memo, an action plan, a multi-media presentation, a survey, or an evaluation study. Some nursing programs may require students to select a peer-reviewed professional nursing journal as the publication venue for their article on their project paper, query the editor, write their article according to the journal's publication guidelines, and complete the article by the end of the capstone course.

Although the format may vary, all capstone projects are expected to culminate in a scholarly product with evidence of the graduate student's ability to synthesize, analyze, and apply knowledge in ways that advance nursing practice. Example A offers samples of selected components of two capstone projects that illustrate the importance of logical content flow, word choice, clarity, and sentence structure.

The DNP EBP Project Scholarly Paper

According to the American Association of Colleges of Nursing (AACN) (2015), "the Doctor of Nursing Practice (DNP) is widely recognized as one of the discipline's two terminal degrees and the preferred pathway for those seeking preparation at the highest level of nursing practice" (1). Despite national agreement about the value of DNP education, great national support for the practice doctorate, and recognition of the need for an EBP scholarly project that illustrates clinical scholarship (Auerbach 2015), there is considerable variability among the DNP programs throughout the United States, and some confusion about the final project.

In response, the AACN (2010, 2015) has taken a leading role in clarifying the distinction between research-focused and practice-focused scholarship and in defining the standards for scholarship that will generate knowledge in nursing. To ensure consistency of learning across

DNP programs, these standards include clarifying the scope of "the final scholarly project, the level of implementation, the impact on system/practice outcomes, the extent of collaborative efforts, the expected dissemination of findings, and the degree of faculty mentorship/oversight," (2015, 3). The AACN has affirmed that the EBP scholarly project should be entitled "The DNP EBP Project Scholarly Paper," thereby decreasing any confusion with the term "capstone" used at various educational levels (National Organization of Nurse Practitioner Faculties [NONPF] 2013). The DNP Project is not a research dissertation and should not be referred to as a dissertation, according to the AACN.

Similar to a capstone project, the format of a DNP project scholarly paper can vary by the academic institution or the doctoral student's practice area, and it may involve both individual and group work. Although innovation is generally encouraged in the design of these projects, the AACN is very clear that the critical elements of a DNP project—planning, implementation, and evaluation—*should be the same for all DNP students*. The essential requirements include the following:

(1) A focus on a change that affects healthcare outcomes either through direct or indirect care,

(2) A micro, meso, or macro level systems or population/aggregate focus,

(3) Implementation in the appropriate arena or area of practice,

(4) A plan for sustainability in financial, systems, or political realities, and not only theoretical abstractions,

(5) An evaluation of processes and/or outcomes (formative or summative) that will guide practice and policy, and

(6) A foundation for future practice scholarship. (AACN 2015, 4)

The AACN is also clear that integrative or systematic reviews or the work in any student portfolio does notequal, nor does it qualify as a DNP project.

Example of Classic DNP EBP Project Scholarly Paper Format

> *Chapter 1*—A general introduction to the EBP project that includes a synopsis of the problem, including a background discussion of the problem that builds the case for addressing the problem. The narrative proceeds from the general to the specific. The problem is stated in one clear, concise sentence that ensures linkage to the project's purpose or

envisioned outcome. In a second clear concise sentence, the purpose (usually in Population Intervention Comparison Outcomes Timeframe (PICOT) format) clarifies for the reader-who-does-not-know, the intent of the project director engaging in project implementation. A short segment about project design and another justifying the selection of either a cost-benefit analysis or a cost-effectiveness analysis sets the stage for the project discussion. This begins with a detailed discussion of the conceptual model or framework and includes a graphic representation of conceptual components as they relate to the EBP project. Definition of terms, assumptions, and limitations follow, along with the project's envisioned significance and a conclusion that transitions the reader to the next chapter. Example B provides an exemplar of a Chapter 1 segment that illustrates logical thought and good writing mechanics.

Chapter 2—Each chapter stands alone with the reader re-oriented to the project topic, problem, and purpose. A comprehensive literature review, which identifies the databases searched, analyzes the relevant literature, identifies the gaps in the literature, and describes how the proposed study will fill those gaps. A graphic representation of the article selection project process clarifies the project director's robust article selection search. The body of this section requires a thorough evaluation of evidence, grouped topic by topic with appropriate sub-topics addressed. Each study must be compared and contrasted with key concepts synthesized based on strengths, weakness, and gaps supportive to the EBP project. Studies should be compared and contrasted with each other in a demonstration if rigorous critical analysis and synthesis. Example C contains an exemplar of a thorough article review with synthesis to another article and the EBP project.

Chapter 3—The methodology chapter first reorients the reader to the problem and purpose, then describes the study design, intervention/innovation criteria, and how the design will achieve the project's purpose. A detailed description of the setting including a robust organizational assessment provides support for project sustainability and includes a SWOT analysis. The project sample and sampling plan offer subject characteristics, inclusion/exclusion criteria, protection of human rights, the setting for the study, data collection methods, instrumentation, equipment, data analysis, and methods for ensuring validity and generalizability, as applicable. Example D offers a sample of selected excerpts from a Chapter 3 EBP Project.

Chapter 4—Again, short statements that reorient the reader to the problem and purpose, then introduce chapter content. Discuss data cleaning and preparation including integrity checks, missing data analysis, and any recoding of variables. Univariate findings may best be presented in tables or graphs that note reliability testing results as appropriate, with bivariate findings presenting the statistical method(s). A completed cost-benefit or cost-effectiveness analysis precedes the chapter conclusion.

Chapter 5—Following reader re-orientation, findings are presented along with a full discussion of those results. Supportive details that underpin findings are presented and linked to the conceptual model, prior literature, contemporary clinical practice and/or organizational procedures that impact clinical outcomes. Following a discussion of project limitations and significance, the project director discusses any implications related to the cost-benefit or the cost-analysis. Chapter 5 may also discuss major conclusions from the EBP project, envisioned practice changes, and recommendations for future EBP project development. Depending on the academic program, a separate chapter, Chapter 6, may be reserved for this discussion.

(*Adapted from*: Melnyk and Fineout-Overholt 2019; The Catholic University of America Conway School of Nursing 2019)

The DNP EBP project scholarly paper is similar to the capstone project paper in that no single format applies to the end product of the work. Neither the AACN nor the National Organization of Nurse Practitioner Faculties (NONPF) has specified a required format, but both offer a number of options for disseminating results that are as varied as the content of the EBP project scholarly paper, institutional policies, and individual program requirements.

Three appendices offer samples of selected components of a DNP EBP Project Scholarly Paper that illustrate the importance of logical content flow, word choice, clarity and good sentence structure for Chapter 1 (Example B), Chapter 2 (Example C), and Chapter 3 (Example D).

The Two-page EBP Project Proposal

Preparing for an oral defense of an EBP Project proposal usually requires a tightly written two-page narrative that includes specific segments of the first three chapters of the DNP student's EBP project. Key to the success in developing this document is the presence of a logical flow of information, excellent sentence structure, and exceptional

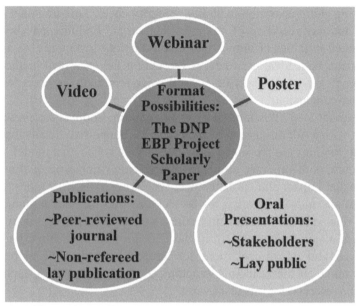

Figure 4.1. *Possible Formats For Disseminating EBP Project Results.*

grammar devoid of any grammatical errors. Students with weak writing proficiency struggle in writing the three chapters and also in developing the two-page narrative. Example E contains an exemplar DNP EBP project two-page proposal that illustrates a logical flow, compressed content contained in well-structured sentences, good word choice, and good writing mechanics.

The PhD Dissertation

Completion of a PhD program, according to the AACN (2015), prepares nurses to generate knowledge through rigorous research and statistical methodologies that may be broadly applicable or generalizable. Since 2010, more than 6000 American nurses have completed the prerequisite graduate studies and a doctoral dissertation and have been awarded a Doctor of Philosophy degree (PhD, Ph.D., or Dphil), which ranks as the highest academic degree awarded by universities worldwide.

In contrast to the more flexible formats used for capstone and DNP projects, the doctoral dissertation is a highly structured scholarly work steeped in rich history. According to Kennedy (2019), the word dissertation (from the Latin word *dissertare*, meaning to debate or examine) first appeared in the English language in 1651 as "an extended written treatment of a subject," and "a substantial paper that is typically based on original research and gives evidence of the candidate's mastery both of her own subject and of scholarly method," (1). That scholarship, said Kennedy (2019), means that a doctoral student does more reading and research than what is expected in undergraduate study; and that the work displays "accuracy and skill in investigation and discussion of subject, which provides evidence of critical analysis and understanding of particular theories or viewpoints that are open to question," (2).

It is possible that the thousands of American nurses who have studied for years and have now completed their PhD dissertations may be unaware that their dissertation research has continued a long international tradition of advanced scholarship that dates back to medieval times. Around 1150 in medieval Paris, records reveal the awarding of the first doctoral degree, with the first doctorate of philosophy degree emerged in Germany as the terminal teacher's credential around 1652 (Noble 2001). In North America, Yale University awarded the first three earned PhDs in 1861 (Rosenberg 1961), and in the United Kingdom, the first modern doctorate was awarded at Durham University in 1882 (Barnes 2013).

Beyond common historical roots, dissertation formats can include some institution-specific house styles, and a number of field-specific, national, and international standards and recommendations for presentation. Despite those variations, PhD dissertations in today's American nursing schools and most dissertations around the world share a long-standing tradition of organizing dissertations with a classic five or six-chapter format, as shown below.

Classic or Traditional Dissertation Format

Chapter 1—A synopsis of the condition that gives rise to the issue of concern launches the full discussion of the background of the problem, which effectively justifies the researcher's case for addressing the problem. The narrative proceeds from the general to the specific with the problem stated in one clear, concise sentence and language that links it to the purpose of the research, which is also conveyed in one clear, concise sentence. There is a brief description of the research design, and a detailed discussion of the conceptual model or framework that includes a graphic representation of conceptual model components as they relate research project. Definition of terms include operational and conceptual definitions followed by assumptions and limitations, study significance, and a conclusion that transitions the reader to the next chapter. Example G provides an exemplar Chapter 1 segment that illustrates logical thought and good writing mechanics.

Chapter 2—Begins with re-acquainting the reader to the study's topic/problem/purpose, then orients the reader to the scope of the literature review. This includes identifying accessed databases, keywords, dissertation abstracts, and eligibility criteria for inclusion and exclusion of literature. A graphic depicts the process for article selection and notes how the references in the selected articles will be reviewed. Gaps in the literature emerge for detailed discussion and justification of the need for the proposed research. A conclusive but robust summary of cogent chapter components follows with a transition statement to the next chapter. Example H contains an exemplar of a literature review segment that demonstrates critical analysis, evaluation, and synthesis.

Chapter 3—After reorienting the reader to Chapter 2, a clear and in-depth discussion of the design includes how the design will answer the research questions. The setting, sample, sampling plan, and size clarify participant selection and the potential participant pool. The participant recruitment process and procedures precede a robust, detailed discussion related to the protection of human subjects and data handling. The next detailed discussion includes instrumentation and use or development of measurement tools. Data collection procedures detail initial participant point-of-contact to procedure completion. Pilot study processes are explained in detail, if applicable. Secondary data collection mirrors the primary data collection components. The data analysis section presents the transformation of raw data into research findings. This includes data cleaning and preparation, providing a descriptive analysis, addressing validity and generalizability, and offering a robust chapter conclusion. Example I offers an example of a logical presentation of methodology for the reader-who-does-not-know.

Chapter 4—This chapter reorients the reader and reports the study findings by addressing each research question individually, offering detailed results and a chapter conclusion that transitions the reader to the final chapter. Example J provides a segment that demonstrates how chapter content can be organized.

Chapter 5—An inclusive discussion chapter that offers a detailed review of results in the context of the literature review and discusses major study conclusions, the implications of the study results for practice, and the investigator's recommendations for future research. Example K offers a sample of this chapter that illustrates logical flow, clarity, and conciseness of thought.

(*Adapted from*: Rudestam and Newton 2007; Johnson, Goodman, and Robert 2019)

Some institutions alter this classic format, particularly in final chapters. This might involve linking the results to the literature in Chapter 4, instead of Chapter 5, and combining Chapter 5 and 6.

Example F offers a sample of selected components of a PhD dissertation for Chapter 1; Example G offers the same for Chapter 3, Example H for Chapter 4, and Example J for Chapter 5. Each illustrates the importance of logical flow, clarity, word choice, and adherence to the basic mechanics of effective writing.

The Two-Page Dissertation Proposal

Similar to an EBP Project Proposal, preparing for an oral defense of the dissertation proposal usually requires a tightly written two-page narrative. Elements critical to success once again include the presence of a logical flow of information, correct sentence structure, and no grammatical errors. Development of this document can be challenging, especially for students who are struggling with writing proficiency. Example K contains an exemplar dissertation two-page proposal that demonstrates a logical flow, well-structured sentences, appropriate word choice, and excellent writing mechanics.

Other Formatting Details

Every university with a PhD program usually publishes its own unique dissertation handbook. This important guide provides doctoral students with critical information about the overall doctoral process, the composition and responsibilities of the dissertation committee, requirements for the dissertation proposal, and formatting guidelines for the dissertation, as well as templates for the dissertation pages and instructions for manual and/or electronic submissions of dissertations.

Doctoral students often find themselves overwhelmed by the excruciating specifications in these formatting guidelines. The handbook traditionally contains the instructions for special pagination of the introductory pages and the regular pages that follow, spacing, types and sizes of fonts, charts and graphs, headings, margins, file formats, and the placement of statements of copyright, signature pages, acknowledgments, dedications, the table of contents, abstract, references, footnotes, endnotes, and citations. Adherence to these detailed specifications enable standardization of dissertations throughout the academic world.

As we discuss in the later chapter on collaboration, independent editors have developed an important niche business helping American doctoral students with this final phase of the dissertation process. Partnering with a highly skilled expert editor who understands formatting sophisticated academic documents makes sense because, with editorial support, doctoral students can focus their time and efforts on research content and the final review of their dissertation and their doctoral defense.

Commonalities

Although different formats for the three major genres of professional writing in nursing research may exist, commonalities among them exist as well: research questions, the literature search, and some essential, non-negotiable writing rules.

Statement of Purpose or Research Questions

One of the most challenging writing tasks for nurse researchers and for most graduate students is writing research questions. According to methodologists Sovacool, Axsen, and Sorrella (2018):

> With some overstatement, getting the research question(s) right could be half the work of writing a good paper. The research question(s) guides a literature review or collection of data, suggests the type of answers a study can give, and provides a strong disciplining device when writing. (13)

Sovacool, Axsen, and Sorrella (2018) offered three very practical tips for writing research questions. First, they suggest building research questions from empirical or conceptual material by conducting a "presearch." No research question can be constructed without reading, they said (14), because "all good research questions are the product of prior engagement with empirical and/or theoretical material." Second, make sure your research question(s) are researchable, that they can be answered with facts and data; and that you are not "chasing a moving target" (Sovacool, Axsen, and Sorrella 2018, 14). A research question that

TABLE 4.1. *Common Errors in Research Questions.*

Poorly Written Research Questions	Problem	Improved Question
How can falls in hospitals be prevented?	Not focused; too broad	What effect do risk assessments for falls have on the incidence of falls?
What can be done about the low percentage of men in the nursing workforce?	Too broad	What are the most effective strategies for recruiting men into nursing?
What are the effects of direct-to-consumer (DTC) marketing campaigns for pharmaceuticals?	Not specific enough	What effect does DTC marketing on patient perceptions of a medication's effectiveness?
Is taking CBD oil bad for health?	Not specific enough	What are the effects of taking CBD oil on the liver function of subjects who use large amounts of CBD oil for pain relief?
Can peer support prevent suicide?	Not focused	Can female suicide prevention relate to elements of peer support?

Adapted from: Sovacool, Axsen, and Sorrella 2018; Johnson, Goodman, and Robert n.d.

can be answered with a yes or no can be very problematic, because it focuses on only one option. Illustrated in Table 4.1 are the most shown in Table 4.1, these are the most common challenges for new researchers who often write research questions that are either too broad or too limited in scope, or that cannot be answered by a single study, which requires clear boundaries and a logical end.

Third, the methodologists emphasize that a research question must be answerable. "A research question needs to be asked in such a way that your expectations can be wrong (and that you know when they are wrong) and that you can be surprised. When confronted with reliable evidence, the answer to the question should be apparent," according to Sovacool, Axsen, and Sorrella (2018, 14).

As shown on the following page, researchers at Harvard University (Poling 2008/2009) created a simple test that can be helpful for assessing if a question is a good research question:

At the end of this chapter, we have included a number of exemplars that provide examples of research questions that in our opinion, qualify as good research questions in nursing research.

Research Questions: Self Test
Does my question allow for many possible answers?
Is it flexible and open-ended?
Is it testable?
Do I know what kind of evidence would allow an answer?
Can I break big "why" questions into empirically resolvable pieces?
Is the question clear and precise?
Do I use vocabulary that is vague or needs definition?
Have I made the premises explicit?
Is it of a scale suitable to the length of the assignment?
Can I explain why the answer matters?

Source: Poling (2008/2009).

Literature Search

One of the most critical, challenging writing requirements common to a capstone project, a DNP project, or a PhD dissertation is the literature search. A high-quality literature review involves far more than merely listing citations from the relevant literature. The 2018 research guidelines from the National Institutes of Health describe a literature review as a "careful assessment of the rigor of the prior research that serves as the key support for a proposed project; identifies any strengths, weaknesses, or specific gaps in the line and rigor of the prior research; and describes how the proposed research addresses the weaknesses in the research," (1). Other definitions by methodologists (Sovacool, Axsen, and Sorrella 2018) framed the literature search as a process for uncovering the themes and nuances of the relevant literature, and for synthesizing perspectives from a variety of disciplines, or from fields with insufficient data.

The key word in this definition is *synthesizing*, which the dictionary defines as a process of making connections among similar elements, combining ideas from many sources, and not merely restating or summarizing. Thus, in a literature review, the graduate student must identify the literature relevant to the research topic and then find the common themes, areas of overlap, and areas of divergence. *The ultimate goal of the literature search is to identify the need for the current research, and to describe how the proposed research adds to the fund of knowledge on a particular topic.* Phrased more simply, conducting a literature review embodies a fundamental feature of positioning oneself in a discipline (Froese, Gantz, and Henry 1998).

Sovacool, Axsen, and Sorrella (2018) describe three basic types of literature reviews that vary in their structure, complexity, and skills required: a *meta-analysis*, a highly structured approach that combines quantitative results across a number of studies on a common topic; a *systematic review*, a structured approach that incorporates both quantitative and qualitative studies, uses explicit search terms and inclusion criteria, and produces a comprehensive, unbiased, and reproducible summary of what is known about a particular topic; and a *narrative review*, the most common type of review and the most susceptible to bias, which is an exploratory evaluation of the existing literature on a particular topic (22–23). Sovacool, Axsen, and Sorrella (2018) suggest that writing a literature review requires an experienced author to uncover nuances in research, and to avoid the biases hidden in the process of including and excluding certain studies in the review, and weighing the evidence from many studies (23).

Given what we know about the writing challenges of nurses, today's nursing faculty cannot assume that graduate nurses have the skills to conduct and write the type of expert literature review that is an *absolute* requirement in high-quality research. According to Lyons and Elmedni (2015), "Instructors in graduate programs bear the responsibility of helping students develop research and writing skills" (38). The faculty cannot assume that a student will learn how to write a literature review on his or her own through self-discovery; that limited expert assistance from the university research librarians (as we discuss in Chapter 12) will be sufficient for the student to develop the required skills in information literacy (Rempel and Davidson 2008); or that requiring students to develop the required skills by reading other literature reviews will be effective as an instructional strategy.

As suggested by Cooke and Murowchick (2014), learning how to write a literature review does not develop naturally for students, who need direct instruction and guided practice that goes beyond acquiring stylistic knowledge and mastering writing fundamentals. Direct instruction is required because as adult learners, graduate students need both direction and support, because they lack competence and may also lack either commitment or confidence (Pratt 1988). Without focused instruction, graduate students typically select poorly defined topics, have inadequate skills in critiquing other research articles, fail to discern important details about differences in methods and outcomes, and summarize relevant articles instead of integrating the findings into the type of sophisticated, scholarly literature review that is required in quality research (Froese, Gantz, and Henry 1998).

Teaching Strategy

Nursing faculty and students can draw upon the large literature on techniques for learning how to write high-quality literature reviews. Some articles detail research on the specific instructional approaches (Cooke and Murowchick 2014; Rempel and Davidson 2008); others offer either a simplified step-by step checklist (Pautasso 2013) or a more systematic approach (Booth, Papaioannou, and Sutton 2012; Machi and McEvoy 2012), whereas many universities offer library guides on literature searches and reviews (Ashford University 2019; Concordia University 2019).

In our experience teaching graduate students, there are core components that are essential in an instructional strategy focused on developing skill in writing literature reviews:

- *A review rubric*—This rubric is a step-by-step guide for critiquing research articles. In a research methods course, this rubric helps students develop their abilities to critically assess the rigor and overall quality of quantitative, qualitative, and mixed method research studies. This process involves asking critical questions about research components. such as sampling procedures (sample size and composition), data collection methods (triangulation of methods and sources), data analysis procedures (statistical methods and content analysis), multiple procedures that ensure validity and reliability, the congruence between the research findings and the authors' conclusions, and limitations of the research.
- *Selection of exemplars*—An important teaching tool is the use of exemplars, or examples of research articles of excellence that demonstrate dimensions of quality. According to To and Carliss (2015), exemplars are useful in helping students to appreciate the characteristics of quality and understand its inherent rigor, which can often seem very abstract, opaque, and difficult to discern. In a classroom setting, analysis of exemplars helps to illustrate the exact words and

concepts that represent important concepts of quality. Sadler (2010) suggested that exemplars help students gain experience in engaging in discussions with teachers and peers about the evaluative process and making judgments about the quality of different research studies. Research by To and Carliss (2015) also found that such discussions ultimately helped students transfer insights from class discussions of exemplars to their own work. However, they warned that for the greatest impact, teachers need to include different types of discussions (such a whole-class, small groups, and peer-to-peer) and also to "react adroitly to on-going interaction with students," (4). To increase their effectiveness as facilitators, educators may need additional training in leading discussions about exemplars in research (Hendry *et al.* 2012).

- *Partnership with university librarians*—As we discussed in detail in the later chapter on collaboration, university librarians are critical partners in graduate education, and especially in helping students learn how to access the most appropriate literature for their research topic. A high-quality literature review depends upon a student's skillful search of the existing literature, which includes current publications (generally defined as work published within the previous five years) and seminal work, which includes older publications that are especially important to a research topic. Seminal works are the classic works—the "canon" or most influential works within a discipline that generated new ideas and changed the thinking with a specialized field of study. Conducting a successful search requires students to be able to identify what research studies are relevant, how to access the appropriate databases, and most critically, how to discern the quality of all research publications.

- *Instructional Strategy*—It is common for students to feel anxious and overwhelmed by the complexity of the literature review, the widespread technology changes in academia, and the myriad of resources available in today's libraries (Gust 2006). In their recent review of evidence-based instructional strategies for adult learners, McCall, Padron, and Andrews (2018) cited . . . scaffolding as an effective instructional strategy for adult learners that involves "breaking down complicated tasks or skills into small components that can be completed one at a time" (38). This process makes the task less stressful than a "one-shot instruction session" and more manageable, the researchers said. Nursing educators use a scaffolding approach when they provide multiple opportunities for learning that begin with simple concepts and advance toward more complex subjects or tasks. According to Rapchak *et al.* (2015), this could involve skill-based workshops, embedding a librarian within curricula, or by creating discipline collaborative opportunities with other instructors. Such learning opportunities would focus first on analyzing the exemplars—those examples of literature reviews that synthesize and illustrate the words and the writing that symbolize excellence—and then advancing to teaching writing techniques that demonstrate synthesizing large amounts of literature.

Writing Rules

We detail the "nuts and bolts"—the myriad of rules, tips, techniques, and processes of good writing—in Section III of this text. However, this chapter, which describes the differences and commonalities among three major academic writing requirements in advanced nursing education, would be incomplete without a reminder about some important rules that apply to all three genres of professional writing. To ensure a high quality of scholarly writing, nurse authors should avoid the following:

- *Personal pronouns*—Unless you are using a case study format with a single individual subject, do not use personal pronouns (such as *you, he, she, it, we, they, me, him, her, us*, and *them*) as either the subject or object of a sentence. Use a noun whenever possible, such as "the patients," "the staff," or "the researchers" instead of "they."
- *Colloquial words or expressions*—Although simplicity in writing is valued in scholarship, scholarly writing uses standard, grammatical English. Scholarly writing is formal and is not the way we typically speak in everyday life. Thus, it is best to avoid all colloquial words, phrases, or sayings from everyday language and casual conversation, as well as slang, profanity, or sexist language. Use of such language can confuse or offend your reading audience and can have a negative effect on your credibility as a writer and a scholar. There are two exceptions to this rule. *First*, in qualitative research, quotes from one-to-one interviews or focus groups must be reported verbatim, without any editing. *Second*, an excerpt with potentially inflammatory language from an interview or focus group may be quoted when a researcher determines that such an excerpt is the most powerful way to illustrate a critical concept. On occasion, however, univer-

sity-specific rules that govern academic writing may require some censoring of inflammatory words. This involves inserting symbols as placeholders for the original letters such as "&x#$!."

- *Jargon*—Like all professions, nursing has its own unique jargon, those unique, specialized "insider" words or expressions used and understood by nurses for efficiency of communication among themselves, but often meaningless to those not in nursing. Nordquist (2019) cited critics of jargon who advised that "most jargon can be replaced with simple, direct language without sacrificing meaning," (1). This is good advice for all nurse authors.

- *Contractions*—As reported by Lee (2015) for the American Psychological Association, whose style guidelines (2010) provide the direction for scholarly writing in social science and nursing, contractions (such as *don't, can't,* or *shouldn't*) should be avoided in formal, scholarly writing. The exception is the same as that for slang or offensive language, i.e., when reported within a direct quote from a research subject or a subject's use of a common idiom such as ". . . Don't count your chickens before they hatch."

- *Use of the term "the researcher"*—Graduate students who have been warned by their advisors not to use passive voice in their writing ("Interviews were conducted.") often resort to using "the researcher" as the subject of a sentence. Use of this term is awkward and unnecessary. Instead of saying . . ." The researcher conducted one-to-one interviews," an author could say . . ." Data collection included one-to-one interviews and a demographic survey."

Developing an Abstract

Each university's requirements differ; however, many require the development of an abstract as part of either the final project paper or the dissertation. Abstracts offer readers an *overview* of the Capstone or EBP project paper, or the dissertation. Although the length of an abstract varies, the traditional range of 250 to 500 words limits the narrative. This can pose problems for writers who struggle to achieve clarity and concise expression, requiring repeated revision and editing.

Remember, an abstract is intended to describe the content of the paper, *not evaluate or defend* its content. The sole aim of an abstract is to assist the reader to "decide whether to read the entire dissertation" or project paper (George Mason University 2019, 1).

Similar to chapter introductions, the abstract should offer a concise statement of the problem and purpose of the work followed by a segment describing aims, design and methodology, major findings, conclusions, and significance. It should not mirror the two-page proposal, but instead relate what the project or research intended to demonstrate. The work accomplished should be described in modest detail. Example L offers an example of an abstract that illustrates a concise and logical flow and clarity and effectively summarizes the dissertation effort.

Preparing the Capstone Project paper, the DNP EBP Project Scholarly Paper, and the PhD Dissertation requires a clear understanding of the different types of academic writing that mark each of these degree requirements. This chapter offered writing rules or writing rubrics and discussed the traditional components of each type of manuscript. In addition, selected exemplar samples illustrated the effectiveness of good writing mechanics, word choice, and logical flow. Finally, the student must clearly understand and adhere to their specific university requirements, which may vary based on program design and expected academic rigor.

Example A: Excerpted from Capstone Project Paper #1; Diabetes Intervention of Hispanic Adults; An EBP Capstone Project Paper; *Courtesy of:* Carey M. DeLuca, MSN, APRN, FNP-C, A-GNP PC-C, 2019

Clinical Problem Scenario

A nurse practitioner (NP) works in a community clinic that serves primarily Hispanic patients in Washington D.C. Over the past year, the NP has noticed that many appointments relate to the diagnosis and management of type 2 diabetes. During the appointments, he explores concerns, performs physical exams, and orders routine blood work. The blood work results of many patients reveal elevated glycosylated hemoglobin A1c levels (HA1c) (>8%). The NP assigns a diagnosis of type 2 diabetes and begins the steps to manage the disease. The diagnosis of diabetes frequently frightens Hispanic patients. Many report knowing a family member or friend with the disease and recognize diabetes is something negative. Others believe that since their family members have the disease, it is only natural that they will receive the same diagnosis.

A prescription of Metformin 500–1000 mg twice a day and lifestyle modification serves as firstline treatment. The NP provides all the required information to the patient about the disease and its management during the brief appointment. Upon returning to the clinic for a three-month follow-up appointment, the patient reports no change in lifestyle and minimal compliance to the recommended pharmacological treatment. Unfortunately, the patient's HA1c remains elevated. Barriers to diabetes management in the Hispanic population include language barriers, difficulties navigating the U.S. healthcare system and obtaining insurance, and illiteracy. Time, work constraints, familial expectations and obligations also present barriers to participation in one's own healthcare.

Clinical PICO Question

What are the best evidence-based interventions to improve HA1c levels in Hispanic adults in a primary care setting?

Population Intervention Comparison Outcomes (PICO):

P—Male and female Hispanic patients with a new and or an existing diagnosis of type 2 diabetes at a community clinic in Washington D.C.

I—Literacy-sensitive, culturally tailored, monthly type 2 diabetes self-management group education course with a community health care provider (e.g., nurse, CHW, or NP)

C—Usual management of type 2 diabetes for this population.

O—Decrease in patient HA1c levels (primary); increased knowledge about diabetes risk factors and disease management, such as, diabetes knowledge, diabetes medication compliance, increased compliance with lifestyle modification (i.e., diet and exercise) (secondary).

Evidenced Based Recommendations

Four main common themes emerged from the evaluation of the literature in which recommendations for clinical practice can be made for this population. First, the literature found that Hispanic patients learn better about type 2 diabetes self-management in a weekly or monthly group education classes compared to individualized learning at home or with the provider at a health appointment. Augmenting group learning with the assistance of a CHW or community religious Figure who provides regular teaching per recommended guidelines (i.e., American Diabetes Association and USPTF) and regularly follows up with patients in between group classes improves outcomes in diabetes.

Per the literature, implementation of these diabetes group education classes increased diabetes knowledge, reduced HA1c levels and increased compliance with other diabetes benchmarks (e.g., eye exam, foot exam, physical activity). Second, the literature revealed the importance of developing literacy-sensitive, culturally-tailored learning environments in the Spanish language. All the literature explored emphasized the use of a culturally-sensitive dynamic teaching approach with an educational leader to foster inclusivity and interest in learning about diabetes to reduce HA1c levels, improve diabetes knowledge, and ensure disease management compliance. Such approaches included small-group discussion on diabetes management and goal setting.

More dynamic education approaches included learning and performing home exercises, watching a telenovela on diabetes management, and collectively cooking a healthy-version of typical Hispanic meal as group. The use of the SKILLD or DKQ-24 diabetes assessment tools, that are literacy-sensitive and in Spanish, provided a method for measuring knowledge acquisition in this population pre and post intervention. Third, the inclusion of family members in group programs may promote continued compliance and encouragement with a patient's diabetes self-management. Having a family member who understands the nature of the disease and the consequences of poor glycemic control is more likely to be supportive than someone who has limited knowledge of the disease process.

Fourth, additional studies are needed for evaluation of type 2 diabetes self-management in the long-term. Most of the studies reviewed examined interventions for less than one year. At the one-year mark in some of the studies, the positive effects of the intervention decreased. It is important to develop measures that check in with patients after the diabetes education program to ensure they are still implementing healthy behaviors and properly managing the disease. Since diabetes is a chronic disease, the establishment of longer intervention times allows providers to better trend HA1c changes, since changes to HA1c results occur over time.

Excerpted from Capstone Project Paper #2:
Best Evidence-Based Interventions to Improve Appointment
Adherence in Adult Multiple Sclerosis Patients
Courtesy of: **Erica Wiles, MSN, APRN, A-GNP PC, 2019**

When compared to other patient populations, those with Multiple

Sclerosis (MS) are at an increased risk for poor long-term adherence to treatment and appointments. A high percentage of patients who miss scheduled appointments may inevitably lose follow-up care thereafter. Therefore, it is important to find effective ways to improve appointment adherence in the multiple sclerosis veteran patient population.

Problem in PICO Question Format

The question for providers is "What best evidence-based interventions improve appointment adherence in multiple sclerosis patients?

The evidence-based practice review consists of the population of adult veterans diagnosed with multiple sclerosis. The desired outcome is a statistically significant improvement in appointment adherence for this patient population.

Evidenced-Based Recommendations

Analysis of existing research literature suggests that the following recommendations may increase appointment adherence in the MS veteran patient population. First, healthcare providers and additional staff in the MS clinic would receive weekly training during morning group huddle to learn the critical information for patient discussion during each appointment as noted in Example B. A generated appointment sheet noting appointment 2 or 3 days prior to the scheduled appointment day will be by the clinic secretary and nurse to contact patients prior to their appointment day. If 100% of calls are made each month a free lunch will be provided on the first Friday of the following month for the clinic team. Both the secretary and MS nurse in the clinic are responsible to make phone calls two days prior to appointment *if* the appointment falls on a Wednesday, Thursday, or Friday. Patients scheduled on Mondays and Tuesdays will be contacted the Friday before the scheduled appointment time. Additional staff members will be trained as back-up staff if the secretary or MS nurse cannot fulfill the call function.

The staff member will call the phone number attached to the patient's chart. If there is no answer, they will record a voicemail if possible. Example C contains the script. During clinic visits, patients will discuss the callback system for appointment information. See Example B for discussion topics. The project director will conduct a retrospective review weekly each Friday to confirm completed calls and review the number of "kept" scheduled patient appointments versus total number of scheduled appointments. Retrospective data collection will include the percentage of calls made for each scheduled appointment by MS nursing staff and the % of patients who came to scheduled appointment to assess no-shows.

Conclusion

Appointment adherence within the multiple sclerosis veteran patient population is an important problem to address. Multiple sclerosis related cognitive and emotional difficulties leads to an increase risk for poor long-term adherence to treatments and follow up healthcare. Research literature suggests using a short message service system to increase appointment adherence. Utilizing a callback system aims to increase appointment adherence over 3, 6, 9, and 12 months post intervention. Outcome measures will identify statistical measurements regarding appointment adherence and treatment adherence. Continued implementation and outcome measurements will determine the effectiveness of this evidence-based intervention.

Example B: Excerpted from EBP Scholarly Paper Chapter 1; Identification of Primary Care Nurse Practitioner Procedural Skills Used in Practice; *Courtesy of:* David R. Want, MSN, FNP-C, RN, CCRN, 2019

The Consensus Model for Advanced Practice Registered Nurse (APRN) regulation delineates four APRN roles: Certified Nurse Midwife (CNM), Certified Registered Nurse Anesthetist (CRNA), Clinical Nurse Specialist (CNS), and Nurse Practitioner (NP) (APRN Consensus Work Group 2008). Per the 2008 National Sample Survey of Registered Nurses, NPs comprise the largest of the four APRN roles (U.S. Department of Health and Human Services, Health Resources and Services Administration, 2010). According to the 2019 American Association of Nurse Practitioners (AANP) Fact Sheet, the number of licensed NPs in the United States now exceeds 270,000 (NPFacts 2019). The rapidly growing field includes approximately 26,000 newly graduated NPs between 2016 and 2017. NPs now hold prescriptive authority in all fifty states, the District of Columbia (DC), and three territories. Each state/ jurisdiction constitutes varying practice environments, defined by each's laws and regulations, and the manner in which they shape NP scope of practice.

In their "Population-Focused Nurse Practitioner Competencies (2013), NONPF offers non-binding recommendations regarding curricular CPS content. NONPF recommends that FNP programs teach CPS related to (procedures such as) suturing, lesion removal, incision and drainage, casting/splinting, microscopy, and gynecology procedures (NONFP 2013). Ideally, mastery of these competencies within their NP program adequately prepares the NP to perform the skills commonly encountered in the care of the specific population. However, as NPs transition to practice, the literature supports that NPs report self-perceived lack of preparation in CPS (Hart and Macnee 2007; Hart and Bowen 2016). Moreover, although the NPs received training in their academic NP program in CPS recommended by NONPF, in practice, the NPs were being required to perform additional CPS.

Factors influencing the exposure of NPs to CPS not included in their program of study include the care of patients with a wide diversity of acuities whose care and management requires competence in multiple CPS, and the placement of NPs in settings or specialties providing care for a specific subset of patients for which the NP received minimal training. For example, an Adult-Gerontology Acute Care NP (AGAC-NP) provides care to patients with unstable chronic, complex acute, and critical conditions in a variety of settings, such as intensive care, emergency care, the home, or any inpatient unit (NONPF 2012). To provide care for patients with such high acuity requires competency in CPS such as intubation, lumbar puncture, and cardioversion—skills not taught in all NP programs (Kleinpell *et al.* 2006).

The literature supports that NPs who lack the core CPS essential to their practice setting risk practicing beyond their skill set, thus exposing themselves to liability, and their patients to risk of iatrogenic harm. The data furnished by this project will aid in clarifying the CPS used most often, and considered most critical, to various geographic practice settings and patient populations. This, in turn, aids in the revision of curricular standards and guidelines, to ensure that primary care NP education teaches core essential CPS that NPs need within their practice setting and for their patient population, increasing NPs preparedness to perform quality CPS and thus improving patient safety.

Example C: Excerpted from EBP Scholarly Paper Chapter 2; Identification of Primary Care Nurse Practitioner Procedural Skills Used in Practice; *Courtesy of:* David R. Want, MSN, FNP-C, RN, CCRN

Kleinpell *et al.* (2006) conducted a non-experimental descriptive survey of program directors of 56 Acute Care Nurse Practitioner (ACNP) programs. The study sought to identify skills taught in ACNP programs and to query regarding the importance of teaching the skills. The authors developed a new skills questionnaire inclusive of skills based on a literature review, the scope and standards of ACNP practice, and ACNP role descriptions (Kleinpell *et al.* 2006). The questionnaire included 70 skills. The respondent indicated whether they taught the skill, and whether to teach the skill, and rate the importance of the skill on a scale of 1 – 5 (1 = low and 5 = high). Kleinpell disseminated the survey via e-mail to program directors across the U.S. Results indicated that the most frequently taught skills included EKG interpretation (100%), chest X-ray interpretation (98%), hemodynamic monitoring (91%), suturing (89%), spirometry and peak flow assessment (78%). The least frequently taught skills included superficial abscess incision and drainage and wound packing (41%), IAPB management (45%), discontinuation of chest tubes (46%), and chest tube insertion, endotracheal intubation, and wound debridement (48%).

Respondent recommended the teaching of the following skills: EKG and chest X-ray interpretation ($n = 44$), hemodynamic monitoring ($n = 40$), and suturing ($n = 41$). Respondents recommended against the teaching of the following: wound packing ($n = 19$), IAPB management ($n = 17$), discontinuation of chest tubes and intercranial pressure monitoring ($n = 16$), and chest tube insertion, wound debridement, and superficial abscess incision and drainage ($n = 14$). Skills rated as highly important (rated as 5) to teach in an ACNP program included: EKG interpretation ($n = 44$), X-ray interpretation ($n = 42$), hemodynamic monitoring ($n = 36$), and suturing ($n = 33$).

Skills rated as having low importance (rated as 1) included: esophageal doppler intubation, umbilical artery cannulation, and umbilical vein cannulation ($n = 20$), fasciotomy ($n = 17$), suprapubic bladder aspiration ($n = 16$), and bone marrow aspiration and percutaneous endoscopic gastrostomy ($n = 15$). Study strengths included a large sample size, a national survey, and a large listing of CPS. Weaknesses included the inclusion of only program directors and not faculty and students, lack of a robust literature review to substantiate need for study, failure to identify how they identified the program directors, the use of a newly-developed questionnaire without content validity, focus limited to ACNP programs, and lack of demographic information regarding the directors and their programs. As the previous study, this study provided evidence on the types of CPS taught in ACNP programs and the directors' perception of whether to teach the CPS, and the level of importance of teaching the CPS in the ACNP program. However, this study only focused on program directors and not on graduates and what skills they perform in practice.

In addition, the study focused only on ACNP programs and not other types of NP programs. This project will survey NPs across a broad range of specialties, include CPS relevant to various types of NPs and clinic settings, and directly survey NPs to identify the importance, frequency of performance of the skill or procedure in the NP's clinical practice and where the NP received initial training on the CPS. This article demonstrates a strength of Level III non-experimental, and a quality of C, per the JHNEBP evidence rating scale (Dang and Dearholt, 2017).

Example D: Excerpted from EBP Scholarly Paper Chapter 3; Identification of Primary Care Nurse Practitioner Procedural Skills Used in Practice; *Courtesy of:* **David R. Want, MSN, FNP-C, RN, CCRN**

Procedures for Data Analysis

Cleaning and Preparing the Data

To clean and prepare the data, the project director will use frequency analysis to check for errors, outliers, and missing data. Any cases missing greater than 10% of the data will not be included in the analysis. The patterns of missing data will be analyzed using the missing completely at random (MCAR) Little's statistical test and multiple imputation will be used to correct missing values. The reliability of the PCCSSI will be tested using the Cronbach alpha coefficient statistic.

Univariate Analysis

Descriptive statistics will present sample and variable characteristics. Since the data is categorical with the exception of the number of years of nursing practice, frequencies and percentages will be reported. Additionally, frequencies and percentages will be reported for the following variables: importance of clinical skill or procedure to practice, frequency of performance of the procedure and skill, and location of acquisition of the skill or procedure.

Further analysis will be conducted to assess specific percentages within each of the main variables: frequency of use of the CPS, importance of the CPS, and location of the acquisition of the training for the CPS. First, analysis of the frequency of use of the CPS by greater than

50% of respondents will be assessed with analysis of the percentage of the NPs who indicated that they learned the skill or procedure in their NP program. Next, analysis of the CPS used by less than 10% of NPs will be completed.

Next, analysis of the CPS used by greater than 50% of the respondents and their overall percentage of frequency of use (routinely, frequently, or rarely) will be completed. In terms of importance, analysis of the importance of the CPS used by greater than 50% of respondents with analysis of the percentage of the NPs who indicated that they learned the skill or procedure in their NP program. Finally, analysis of the CPS used rarely ("once every six months") but rated as important or very important will be completed with inclusion of analysis of the percentage of the NPs who indicated they learned skill or procedure in their NP program.

Conclusion

As previously stated, there exist gaps in the literature with regard to the CPS used most often and most critical to practice, and thus which to teach. This knowledge deficit drives the selection of non-experimental, exploratory methodology. The problem of lack of clarity regarding essential CPS for primary care NP practice, and the resulting inconsistencies across NP programs, necessitates the identification of CPS used most often and most critical to practice.

The literature recommends that this occur via survey beyond the state level, hence the selection of a cross-sectional survey methodology. The data gathered by this project provides a seminal appraisal of the state of NP CPS in one region of the U.S., with dissemination of findings planned to occur via publication and presentation at regional and national conferences, such as the NONPF conference, or the AANP conference. The data further drives formation of a list of core CPS for primary care NPs to guide standardization of CPS curricular requirements.

Example E: Two-Page EBP Project Proposal; Identification of Primary Care Nurse Practitioner Procedural Skills Used in Practice; *Courtesy of:* **David R. Want, MSN, FNP-C, RN, CCRN**

Introduction

Primary care nurse practitioner (NP) programs prepare students to practice in a variety of settings, such as the low acuity section of emergency departments, urgent care centers, isolated rural clinics, specialty practices, large group practices, or as solo providers. A wide variety of clinical procedural skills (CPS) are required by these differing settings. In 2013, the National Organization of Nurse Practitioner Faculties (NONPF) released the Population-Focused Nurse Practitioner Competencies, which included a list of CPS for inclusion in curricula. This list suggests—but does not require—that NP programs teach CPS "which may include, but are not limited to, suturing, lesion removal, incision and drainage, casting/splinting, microscopy, and gynecology procedures." NP curricular guidelines lack clarity and uniformity regarding which specific CPS to teach, resulting in inconsistent requirements across NP programs (Scheibmeir, 2015). Additionally, as the types of NP practice settings increases, the author envisions expansion of NP program content. Hence, NP programs must determine the most often used and those considered most critical in order to ensure appropriate student CPS acquisition prior to graduation.

Purpose

This project aims to describe the current use of primary care NP CPS and establish baseline knowledge of CPS utilized in primary care NP practice. Generated data will assist in guiding and standardizing CPS curricular requirements. This project will survey a regional sample of NPs working in primary, urgent, low acuity emergency, and specialty care settings to determine which CPS they use most often (frequency), which CPS they consider most important (importance), and whether they received CPS training in their NP program or after entry to practice (training). This project operationalizes importance as a skill or procedure's criticality to a NP's practice, the absence of which render the NP unable to care for the patient, necessitating referral to another provider. This project operationalizes frequency as how often an NP typically performs a skill or procedure: at least once a week, at least once a month, at least once every six months, or never.

Literature Review

Relevant literature includes surveys of NP and physician assistant (PA) programs regarding CPS curricular content, and surveys of NPs regarding CPS used in practice. Cole and Ramirez (2003) conducted a descriptive survey of directors of 178 FNP programs regarding CPS with a 64% response rate and identified a misalignment between those CPS that program directors rated as critical and the CPS which were actually taught. Cole and Ramirez's study lacks input from graduates of these programs or any NPs in clinical practice. Cole and Ramirez also recommended that FNP programs survey graduates and practice sites regarding CPS used when making decisions regarding which to teach. Hart and Macnee identified selfperceived deficits in CPS preparation, as well as NP desire for increased CPS preparation rigor and relevance to practice. In 2015, Scheibmeir conducted a descriptive survey of a convenience sample of 297 NP programs (36% response rate) and 125 PA programs (38% response rate) regarding curricular content. Scheibmeir (2015) identified gaps in NP CPS curricular content but the study lacks program demographics (type, size, and geographic setting). Building upon Hart and Macnee's (2007) earlier work, Hart and Bowen (2016) conducted a descriptive study of a convenience sample of 51,000 NPs regarding preparedness upon graduation yielding a 1% response rate. NPs identified CPS as one of the four areas in which they felt least prepared for practice, and Hart and Bowen recommended that these areas of deficit guide curricular changes. Laustsen (2013) surveyed 1450 NPs and concluded that the rural vs. urban geographic practice setting affects CPS utilization. He also suggested NP programs base CPS selection on those used most often and those considered critical to practice. The paucity of evidence regarding the current state of CPS used by primary care NPs, as well as the strength of the recommendations of Laustsen and other researchers, creates a gap that inivites a descriptive study to survey primary care NPs beyond the single state surveyed by Laustsen (2013). Surveying a multistate region that includes a range of urban, suburban, and rural participants, such as the American Association of Nurse Practitioners' (AANP) Region 3, elevates the value and importance of the project to the profession and healthcare field.

Significance

By reporting the most often used CPS and those considered most critical by a multistate sample of NPs, this project will contribute data to national nursing organizations that recommends curricular content and expected competencies of graduates to guide ongoing evaluation and revision of core and population focused competencies. It will also contribute to producing greater congruence between the CPS needs of clinical practice, and the curricular content of NP programs. Through project director knowledge dissemination, this project will inform regional and national stakeholders regarding the current state of primary care CPS and advance consensus regarding primary care NP CPS curricular content.

Theoretical Model

The Five-Stage Model of Adult Skill Acquisition (Dreyfus 2004) posits adult skill acquisition founded upon experiential and situationally-based learning. As students learn and pass through the stages of skill acquisition (novice to expert), they rely heavily on experience and less on theory. Therefore, programs must maximize student CPS experiences. This requires identifying CPS that rank critical to NP practice.

Description of the Methodology and Participants

Instrument

Laustsen (2013) based the PCCSSI on the 90 CPS listed in *Ambulatory Care Procedures for the Nurse Practitioner* (Colyar and Erhardt 2004), and an expert panel of three experienced FNPs evaluated the instrument for content validity. The PCCSSI gathers respondent demographic information including their area of NP certification, level of preparation for initial NP certification, year of initial NP certification, geographic setting of clinical practice, practice size/number of patient visits annually, and age of patient populations. Respondents rate frequency of CPS use, where learned, and importance of CPS.

Modified PCCSSI

Following a revision, the original PCCSSI reflects congruence with a current primary care CPS textbook (Edmunds 2017), and an expert panel of family, pediatric, and adult/gerontological NPs verified content validity.

Participants

Target participants include primary care NPs working with family, adult, and/or pediatric populations. Example A contains the list of possible participants derives from constituent states/jurisdictions of AANP Region 3. Participants will receive an Invitation to Participate (Example B) via email from their state/jurisdiction NP association once a week for a total of four weeks, or view it on their association's website, or social media platform for a period of four weeks. The invitation describes the survey as short, anonymous, and online, and includes the University's Office of Sponsored Programs' and the project director's contact information and a link to the modified PCCSSI (Example C) hosted on Survey Monkey for participant self-administration. To exclude non-NP responses, the invitation notifies and the demographic form requests that NPs confirm their sole focus in primary care prior to completing the survey. To prevent participants from responding more than once, the project director will use the IP addresses collected by Survey Monkey to create unique sequential numeric identifiers for each participant, then delete the IP addresses, ensuring participant anonymity. Prior to agreeing to disseminate the Invitation and after University IRB approval, the project director will seek state-specific NP research/ EBP committee permission.

Data Analysis Plan

Categorical/nominal and ordinal variable analysis includes: Ordinal variables recoding to categorical thereby facilitating bivariate analysis in concert with descriptive analysis of demographic data (frequencies and percentages). Bivariate analysis will examine associations between CPS "training" and "frequency," and between "training" and "importance.", and among all survey respondents, by patient population, and NP certification subgroups. Computed Chi-squared tests of independence will determine if associations exist, and Spearman's Rho or Phi Coefficient/ Cramer's V will explore the strength of relationships. Descriptive analysis (frequencies and percentages) of the following survey variables will include: practice location, practice state/jurisdiction, annual patient visits, educational program type, educational setting, years in practice, hours worked each week. If indicated, bivariate analysis will explore potential associations.

Procedures for Protecting the Anonymity of the Participants

Participants will receive the invitation to participate directly from their state/ jurisdiction and will respond anonymously within a survey period of four weeks. Only the project director will access to the raw data, stored on a password-protected computer, in a locked office. SurveyMonkey (SM) requires multi-factor authentication, the use of virtual private networks or similar forms of secure connectivity, and sufficiently complex passwords and lockouts to prevent reuse upon expiration. Encrypted user data using TLS cryptographic protocols will secure data while in transit, with the encrypted SM system securing data at rest. This exempt project disallows direct participant identification in both recorded information or participant identifiers. As an anonymous survey it creates no risk of harm.

Methods for Ensuring Informed Consent

The invitation to participate (Example B) explains that participant's completion of the project implies their consent to participate, directing those with questions to either the project director, or University's Office of Sponsored Projects.

Example F: Excerpted from PhD Dissertation Chapter 1; Sedentary Behavior and Subjective Wellbeing: A Cross-sectional Study; *Courtesy of:* Elizabeth A. Molle, PhD, MSN, RN-BC, 2019

Sedentary behavior, a distinct subcategory of physical inactivity, poses a new and emerging public health concern. Experts define sedentary behavior as waking behaviors in sitting, reclining or lying positions with minimal energy expenditures (Tremblay *et al.* 2017); whereas inactivity refers to insufficient behavior to meet the World Health Organization physical activity recommendations of 150 minutes of moderate to vigorous activity per week (World Health Organization 2010). According to the Sedentary Behavior Research Network terminology consensus report, sedentary time refers to the "time spent for any duration (e.g., minutes per day) in sedentary behaviors," (Tremblay *et al.* 2017, 9). A definitive amount of time constituting sedentary versus nonsedentary behaviors has not been established. Adults can meet or exceed the public health physical activity guidelines, but concurrently can exhibit high rates of sedentary behaviors (Biswas *et al.* 2015; Milton, Gale, Stamatakis and Bauman, 2015; Sigmundová *et al.*, 2015). For example, adults may participate in exercise classes three nights a week (totaling 150 minutes/week), but may sit eight hours per day at work or home: thus they engage in both sedentary behaviors and physical activity.

The problem with sedentary behaviors occurs from the lack of contractile stimulation of the skeletal muscles resulting in decreasing lipoprotein lipase enzyme activity, which leads to health problems (Engeroff *et al.*, 2017; Peeters *et al.*, 2013). According to Engeroff *et al.* (2017) the "lack of muscle contraction from immobilization leads to suppression of skeletal muscle lipoprotein enzymes and changes energy metabolism" (678). Energy metabolism changes result in increased plasma triacylglycerol levels and decreased insulin sensitivity (Engeroff, *et al.* 2017). Moreover, sedentary behaviors decrease peristalsis and increases colonic transit time, which contributes to untoward health problems (i.e., colon cancer, diabetes, cardiovascular), (Biswas *et al.*, 2015; Cerdá *et al.* 2016; Monda *et al.*, 2017). Furthermore, recent epidemiological and physiological research studies found that sedentary behavior poses health risks irrespective of amount of the physical activity because of physiological changes related to decreased skeletal muscle contractions and changes in the colon (Biswas *et al.*, 2015; Conroy, Maher, Elavsky, Hyde and Doerksen, 2013; Owen *et al.*, 2011; Wilmot *et al.*, 2012).

In addition, the significant impact of sedentary behaviors evidences itself in a negative economic impact as presented in the following two sections beginning with the economic costs. However, caution is warranted as researchers intermingle the definitions of sedentary behavior and inactivity. This researcher summarized the definitions and measurement methods for the sedentary behavior studies used in this study in Example A.

Sedentary Behaviors' Influence on Subjective Wellbeing

Understanding the physiology of the effects of sedentary behavior and the consequent influences on SWB may provide critical insight into understanding the relationship between these two concepts. This section introduces the biological plausibility that explains how sedentary behavior influences SWB and offers the rationale for studying older adults.

Biological Plausibility

According to Gordis (2014) biological plausibility refers to the "coherence with current body of biological knowledge" (251) that supports a temporal cause and effect relationship between two variables. The primary plausibility rests on the premise that sedentary behavior, specifically the act of sitting, decreased peristalsis, which increases the stools connection time with the mucosal layers of the colon (Cerdá *et al.* 2016; Clark and Mach 2016; Conlon and Bird 2015; Monda *et al.* 2017). Peristalsis refers to the involuntary contractile movement of smooth intestinal muscles to propel stool through the colon for defecation (Murillo-Rincon *et al.* 2017). Exercise increases peristalsis while sedentary behavior decreases it. Decreased peristalsis caused by sedentary behavior results in changes in colonic transit time, which poses problems because it changes the gut bacteria. According to gastroenterology experts Lewis and Heaton's (1997) seminal paper, colonic transit time alters the biological growth of organisms in both small and large intestines. Since 1997, multiple gastroenterology experts further support Lewis and Heaton's (1997) claim that colonic transit time alters the gut microbial habitat and microbial composition (Clark and Mach 2016; Murillo-Rincon *et al.* 2017; Tottey *et al.* 2017; Vandeputte *et al.* 2016).

Experts refer to the gut microbial composition as the gut microbiome and its imbalance or alterations as gut dysbiosis (Cerdá *et al.* 2016; Clark and Mach 2016; Monda *et al.* 2017; Vandeputte *et al.* 2016). Science supports that the gut microbiome directly contributes to the complex neurochemical pathways that influences the central nervous system (Cerdá *et al.* 2016; Shiro *et al.* 2017). More specifically, strong evidence supports that certain microbes influence the effectiveness and production of neurotransmitters (i.e., serotonin and dopamine), (Cerdá *et al.* 2016; Choi *et al.* 2013; Monda *et al.* 2017). These neurotransmitters contribute to the feelings of happiness, joy and thus SWB; conversely low levels of serotonin and dopamine result in sadness, loss of joy and thus lower SWB. In summary, gut dysbiosis, caused by sedentary behavior and decreased peristalsis, contribute to changes in the effectiveness of neurotransmitters thus impact SWB. More convincingly, evidence from clinical research studies provide early support that sedentary behaviors change the gut microbiome.

For example, Allen *et al.* (2017), conducted a small pilot study ($N = 32$) of sedentary adults (defined as less than 30 minutes of activity per week) with a crossover design (six-weeks of endurance training to and a return to six-weeks of sedentary behavior) with a six-week washout period between endurance training and sedentarism. During the endurance-training period, participants engaged in supervised 30–60 minutes of moderate to vigorous aerobic exercise activity. Researchers instructed participants during the washout period and sedentary time to refrain from all types of exercise and inferred that this meant the participants were sedentary. Allen *et al.* (2017) measured the gut microbiome before the intervention, immediately after the six-week intervention and then again in six weeks. Allen *et al.* (2017) found that exercise changed the microbiota (i.e., beta diversity) which included both functional and compositional changes in the bacteria; more importantly, after the return to sedentary behavior, the composition of the microbiota reverted to its initial state. Findings from the Allen *et al.* (2017) empirical study, albeit a small sample, further supported Clark and Mach (2016), Lewis and Heaton (1997) and Vandeputte *et al.* (2016) that sedentary behaviors contributes to the changes in the gut microbiota.

Another study, Bressa *et al.* (2017) supports the science behind the biological plausibility postulation that sedentary behavior changes the composition of the gut microbiome. Bressa *et al.* (2017), in a small (*N* = 40) descriptive study of post-menopausal women, compared the gut microbiome of sedentary woman to physically active woman. Bressa *et al.* (2017) defined adults as sedentary if they did not meet the WHO exercise recommendations of 150 minutes of exercise per week, but adults as physically active if they exercised three hours per week. Bressa *et al.* (2017) measured physical activity and sedentary behavior (< 100 counts/minute) with accelerometers for 7-days. Researchers justified defining sedentary behavior at < 100 counts/minute with accelerometers because evidence suggests that those low counts "typically included activities such as sitting or working quietly (reading or typing on a computer)" (Bressa *et al.*, 2017, p.3). Bressa *et al.* (2017) found higher abundance of certain microbiota among the physically active women compared to highly sedentary woman. Admittedly, the Bressa *et al.* (2017) study lacks an experimental design, however it clearly further supports the other experts' (Allen *et al.*, 2017; Clark & Mach, 2016; Lewis & Heaton, 1997 & Vandeputte *et al.*, 2016) findings that sedentary behavior changes the gut microbiota.

Gut microbiome research remains in its infancy stage and thus specific studies that tested how sedentary behaviors influence SWB via the microbiome through specific microorganisms responsible for dopamine and serotonin remains elusive. Challenges exist to conducting gut microbiome research including cost, feasibility of recruiting participants, stool collection and storage. In addition, important ethical concerns exist including collection, privacy and metagenomic testing of the stool (McQuire *et al.*, 2012; Rhodes, 2016). The following section provides the rationale for why older adults were studied.

Economic Impact

Experts report staggering costs—in the billions of dollars annually—associated with sedentary behavior.

For example, a large ($N = 51,165$) multistage probability sample study merged National Health Information Survey (2004–2010) and the Medical Expenditure Panel Survey (2006–2001) data and estimated the percentage of health care expenditures associated with various levels of physical activity (Carlson, Fulton, Pratt, Yang & Adams, 2015). The study included adults over the age of 21 and excluded adults with walking difficulties or pregnancy. According to Carlson *et al.* (2015), sedentary adults account for $117 billion of annual healthcare expenditures after controlling for main covariates (e.g., age, sex, race, and marital status). Carlson *et al.* (2015) defined "sedentary" as insufficiently active or not meeting the recommended 150 minutes of moderate or vigorous activity per week. In addition, experts suggest that sedentary behavior accounts for approximately 11.1% of total healthcare expenditures in the United States. This amounts to approximately $79 billion dollars annually and underscores the importance of studying and addressing the problem of sedentary behavior (Carlson *et al.* 2015). Further support for the financial impact associated with sedentary behavior comes from another large study conducted by Ding *et al.* (2016).

Based on available 2013 data from 187 countries, Ding *et al.* (2016) conducted a global analysis of healthcare costs associated with sedentary behavior and physical inactivity. The researchers defined inactivity as not meeting the WHO requirements of 150 minutes of exercise per week (Ding *et al.*, 2016). Ding et al. (2016) estimated the healthcare costs associated with physical inactivity at $53.8 billion worldwide ($31.2 billion paid by the public sector and $12.9 billion paid by the private sector) for 2013 alone. Furthermore, for the same time period, Ding *et al.* (2016) estimated that the indirect costs associated with sedentarism and inactivity resulted in a worldwide productivity loss of $13.2 billion in 2013. The researchers calculated the productivity loss based on a population attributable fraction cost approach of mortality rates (Ding *et al.*, 2016). Although a search failed to identify costs associated with the specific concept of sedentary behavior, the studies by Ding *et al.* (2016) and Carlson *et al.* (2015) verify the staggering costs associated with limited physical activity and sedentary behavior. More importantly, this behavior also poses untoward health outcomes.

Example G: Excerpted from PhD Dissertation Chapter 2; Sedentary Behavior and Subjective Wellbeing; A Cross-sectional Study; *Courtesy of:* **Elizabeth A. Molle, PhD, MSN, RN-BC, 2019**

Exemplars for the Wilson and Cleary Revised Model

The Wilson and Cleary Revised model (WC-R), described in Chapter 1 posited that as sedentary behavior increased, SWB decreased. Briefly, the model stated that functional status (i.e., sedentary behavior) impacted general health perceptions (i.e., SWB), (Wilson & Cleary, 1995). Individual characteristics (i.e., age, comorbidities, gender social desirability) influenced functional status and general health perceptions (Wilson & Cleary, 1995). Since this study relied on the theoretical underpinnings and assumptions of the WC-R, this review provided a brief overview of three exemplar studies that showed statistical path analyses that supported the linear relationship between functional status and general health perceptions. These three studies specifically tested the WC-R assumption that directly linked functional status to general health perceptions.

First, Sexton, Bennett, Fahey and Cahir (2017) tested the WC-R model in a large ($N = 884$) cohort study that consisted of community dwelling older adults ($M = 77.6$ years). The study measured functional status (activities of daily living) to general health perceptions (anxiety and depression). Sexton *et al.* (2017) found that the path model supported the *a priori* hypothesis that functional status had direct effects on general health perceptions ($\chi = 1.46$, $p = 0.91$, RMSEA < 0.001, CFI $= 1.0$). Statistical values of Comparative Fit Index (CFI) and Root Mean Square Error of Approximation (RMSEA) provided objective measurements for the fit of the model to the data collected with smaller RMSEA values indicating better fit with ?0.05 while CFI values closer to one indicated a perfect fit (Field, 2013). Thus, the findings of a small RMSEA and perfect CFI strongly supports that the data collected aligns with the WC-R assumption that functional status has a direct linear relationship to general health perceptions. The study met exemplar status for these reasons: clearly defined variables that link to the WC-R model; large sample size supported with a power analysis; used psychometrically validated instruments; wellarticulated statistical analysis. The Sexton *et al.* (2017) study further supported this research and the WC-R model assumptions.

Second, Shahrbanian, Duquette, Ahmed and Mayo (2016) tested the WC-R model in a small ($N = 188$) cross-sectional study of adults with multiple sclerosis. Shahrbanian *et al.* (2016) measured functional status (i.e., gait speed and recreational activities) to general health perceptions (i.e., anxiety, mood and depression). Shahrbanian *et al.* (2016) found that the path model supported the *a priori* hypothesis that functional status linked to general health perceptions (χ =113.8, p = 0.08, RMSEA = 0.90 95% CI [0.00, 0.05], p = 0.03; SRMR = 0.05). The small RMSEA statistic indicated that the collected data showed an acceptable model fit based on predetermined paths set by the researchers. This study met exemplar status for four reasons: clearly defined the WC-R model and clearly linked the variables; used validated instruments; well-defined statistical analysis and assumption testing; comprehensive results and discussion section. This study added credibility to the findings from Sexton's *et al.* (2017) study that a direct link existed between functional status and general health perceptions. Therefore, the Shahrbanian *et al.* (2016) study further supports this research that tested the relationship between sedentary behavior (i.e., functional status) and SWB (i.e., general health perceptions).

Third, Gong and Mayo (2015) tested the WC-R model in a moderate size study (N = 207) in adults with rheumatoid arthritis. Gong and Mayo (2015) measured functional status (i.e., activities of daily living) to general health perceptions (i.e., emotional wellbeing). Gong and Mayo (2016) found that the path model supported the *a priori* hypothesis that functional status links to general health perceptions (χ = 19.331, p = 0.15, RMSEA = 0.44, SRMR = 0.20). The small RMSEA statistic indicates that the data collected in the Gong and Mayo (2015) study supports the WC-R assumption that functional status has direct effects on general health perception. This study met exemplar status for five reasons: clear and well described background information; clearly links the WC-R model to the variables; validated instruments with validity reports for each instrument; well-defined statistical analysis with SEM path modeling; comprehensive results and discussion section. The Gong and Mayo (2015) findings align with the Shahrbanian *et al.*, (2016) and Sexton *et al.* (2017) results.

Hence, collectively these three studies support the assumption of the WC-R model that Wilson & Cleary (1995) posited that functional status has direct effects on general health perceptions and thus further supports the models' use in this research.

Section Summary

Arguably, these three studies differ in populations and variables than this completed research effort; however, Gong and Mayo (2015), Sexton *et al.* (2017), Shahrbanian *et al.* (2016) studies provided empirical evidence for the theoretical underpinnings associated with this conceptual model. Each study used sophisticated path analyses modeling statistics to determine the model fit, which analyzed the collected data to *a priori* hypotheses that functional status directly influences general health perceptions. These three studies further support the use of the WC-R model for this study. More importantly, they clearly link functional status (i.e., sedentary behavior) to general health perceptions (i.e., SWB). Now, this review discusses and provides evidence that older adult's experience high sedentary behaviors.

Example H: Excerpted from PhD Dissertation Chapter 3; Sedentary Behavior and Subjective Wellbeing; A Cross-sectional Study; *Courtesy of:* Elizabeth A. Molle, PhD, MSN, RN-BC, 2019

Introduction

Sedentary behavior, the act of sitting, reclining or lying while awake, poses health problems because of the physiological changes associated with sitting. The inverse relationship between sedentary behavior and subjective wellbeing (SWB) poses an even more disconcerting problem because it contributes to premature mortality and poses an economic burden to society. This study attempted to address four important aspects related to sedentary behavior and SWB. First, the study aimed to examine the relationship between sedentary behavior and SWB. Second, this study aimed to determine which of the sedentary behavior estimates (weekday and weekend) explained more of SWB. Third, this study aimed to determine if gender moderated the relationship between sedentary behavior and SWB. Last, this study aimed to determine if the amount of sedentary behavior related to differences in stool consistency. Understanding these aims provides critical information necessary to solve the problem of sedentary behaviors influencing SWB among older adults. The review of the literature failed to find evidence to address these questions. This chapter consists of eleven main topics: research design, setting, subject/participant, sample size and recruitment, inclusion criteria, exclusion criteria, protection of human subjects and data handling, instrumentation, procedures for data collection, data analysis, limitations and delimitations and summary, which provide the methodology developed to examine the following research questions and hypotheses.

Research Questions

Theory, empirical evidence from primary research studies and biological plausibility support the following research question and hypotheses. For example, the theoretical underpinnings, Wilson and Cleary Revised model (hereafter WC-R) posit that an inverse 105 relationship exists between functional status (i.e., sedentary behavior) and general health perceptions (i.e., SWB), (Ferrans, Zerwic, Wilbur & Larsen, 2005; Wilson & Cleary, 1995), which empirical studies tested and supported (Gong & Mayo, 2015; Sexton, Bennett, Fahey & Cahir, 2017; Shahrbanian, Duquette, Ahmed & Mayo, 2016). Evidence from primary studies support that a relationship exists between sedentary behavior and SWB (Balboa-Castillo *et al.*, 201; Buman *et al.*, 2010; Ku *et al.*, 2016a; Ku *et al.*, 2016b; Vallance *et al.*, 2013; Vallance *et al.*, 2016). However, four gaps remain: how sedentary behavior influences SWB in community dwelling older adults, how differences in weekday and weekend sedentary behavior explains SWB, if gender moderates the relationship between sedentary behavior and SWB, and if the amount of sedentary behavior relates to differences in stool consistency. Therefore, the following bullets identify the four specific research questions that this study aimed to answer: 1. After controlling for age, comorbidities, gender and social desirability, did sedentary behavior influence SWB in older adults?

1. After controlling for age, comorbidities, and social desirability, which of the sedentary behavior estimates (weekday and weekend) explain more of the SWB?
2. After controlling for age, comorbidities and social desirability, did gender moderate the relationship between sedentary behavior and SWB?
3. Was the amount of sedentary behavior related to differences in stool consistency? (This question was solely intended to provide exploratory information and not designed to measure causality).

Research Design

This study aimed to answer the research questions with a cross-sectional research design based on non-purposive quota sampling. Cross-sectional designs collected participant information at one given point in time (Polit & Beck, 2017). Three reasons provided justification for using this design. First, the approach provided a practical method of collecting information using self-reported instruments. More importantly, sedentary behavior experts recommend researchers use self-reported instruments because they capture contextual information about how the sedentary behavior occurs (Biddle *et al.*, 2016; Chastin *et al.*, 2015) and they pose fewer challenges than accelerometers for older adults (Evenson, Buchner & Morland, 2012). Second, this approach minimizes respondent burden as it allows participants to answer questions during a single visit. Third, this researcher selected this method because Polit and Beck (2017) applauded the economic and financial feasibility of this approach.

Example I: Excerpted from PhD Dissertation Chapter 4; Sedentary Behavior and Subjective Wellbeing; A Cross-sectional Study; *Courtesy of:* Elizabeth A. Molle, PhD, MSN, RN-BC, 2019

Section Summary for Univariate Results

The section started with a broad description of the sample. The study included predominately-white (89.7%) older adults aged 65 to 84 years old with an average age of 74 years old. Most participants were married (50%) and reported having obligations outside the home for approximately three days a week. Participants reported having approximately three ($M = 2.65$) televisions and two ($M = 1.50$) computers in their homes.

In general, the participants self-reported experiencing approximately ten hours per day in sedentary behaviors. Males reported higher sedentary time compared to females for both the weekday and weekends. The largest sedentary behavior occurred from watching television for both males and females. However, differences existed as male reported more sedentary time from traveling whereas females reported low overall traveling time. Males self-reported less SWB compared to females. Overall, the participants reported feeling joyful, enthusiastic and creative. However, the participants self-reported not feeling good–natured, peaceful or useful. Males reported higher comorbidities compared to females, but a wide range of scores existed.

The most frequent comorbidities included diabetes, hypertension and heart disease. The majority (79%) of participants reported at least one desirability tendency. Two males declined to answer the stool consistency question. The majority of the participants reported SCT (55%), but only 12% reported FST.

Normality results found that most variables showed non–normality distributions: age, comorbidities, social desirability and SWB. However, total sedentary behavior showed normal distribution. Weekday and weekend sedentary behaviors showed non–normality distributions. The next section describes the bivariate tests and results.

Bivariate Results

This section provides the results of bivariate tests that describe the relationships between the main study variables. The topics for this section include age, comorbidities, gender, social desirability, comparing types of sedentary behavior, comparing sedentary behavior to SWB, and section summary. The bivariate tests examined the relationships between sedentary behavior and the confounding variables and then SWB and the confounding variables. This researcher used the appropriate parametric or non-parametric testing taking into account the variables distributions.

Age

The first bivariate tests describe the relationship between the variable, age, to the three sedentary rates. Age failed to meet the normality assumption and thus this researcher selected to use the non-parametric test, Spearman rank-order, hereafter referred to as Spearman's rho for describing these relationships.

Total Sedentary Behavior

A positive significant relationship exists between age and total sedentary behavior ($r_s = 0.22$, $p = 0.02$). According to the Cohen, Cohen, West and Aiken (2003) effect size interpretation standards, this relationship represents a small (0.22) effect size. This result indicates that as age increases, sedentary behavior increases, but only accounts for approximately 4% of the variance between age and total sedentary behavior.

Weekday Sedentary Behavior

A positive significant relationship exists between age and weekday sedentary behavior ($r_s = 0.20$, $p = 0.03$). This relationship represents a small (0.20) effect size based on the Cohen (2003) effect size classifications. This result indicates that as age increases, weekday sedentary behavior increases, but it only accounts for approximately 4% of the variance between age and weekday sedentary behavior. The relationship between age and total sedentary behavior was slightly stronger than this relationship.

Weekend Sedentary Behavior

A positive significant relationship exists between age and weekend sedentary behavior ($r_s = 0.25$, $p < .01$). This relationship represents a small (0.25) effect size based on the Cohen *et al.* (2003) effect size classifications. This result indicates that as age increases, weekend sedentary behavior increases and it accounts for approximately 6% of the variance between age and weekend sedentary behavior. The strongest relationship exists between age and weekend sedentary behavior. The weakest relationship exists between age and weekday sedentary behavior.

However, causality cannot be determined due to the cross-sectional methodology and thus these findings do not indicate that age causes sedentary to increase. Nonetheless, the results support that a small, positive relationship exists between age and sedentary behavior. The next bivariate test examines the relationship between comorbidities and sedentary behavior.

Comorbidities

This bivariate test describes the relationship between the confounding variable, comorbidities, and the three sedentary rates. Comorbidities failed to meet the normality assumption and thus this researcher selected to use the non-parametric test, Spearman's rho, to describe these relationships.

Total Sedentary Behavior

A negative non-significant relationship exists between comorbidities and total sedentary behavior ($r_s = -0.05$, $p = 0.13$). This result indicates as comorbidities increases, sedentary behavior decreases, but the relationship failed to meet statistical significance.

Weekday Sedentary Behavior

A negative non-significant relationship exists between comorbidities and weekday sedentary behavior ($r_s = -0.06$, $p = 0.11$). This relationship indicates that as comorbidities increase, weekday sedentary behavior decreases. However, the relationship failed to meet statistical significance.

Weekend Sedentary Behavior

A negative non-significant relationship exists between comorbidities and weekend sedentary behavior ($r_s = -0.03$, $p = 0.24$). This relationship indicates that as comorbidities increase, weekend sedentary behavior decreases. However, the relationship failed to meet statistical significance.

The findings fail to demonstrate that a causal relationship exists between comorbidities and sedentary due to the cross-sectional methodology used in this study. Nonetheless, the results indicate a small negative relationship exists between comorbidities and sedentary behavior. The next bivariate test examines the differences between genders and sedentary behavior.

Example J: Excerpted from PhD Dissertation Chapter 5; Sedentary Behavior and Subjective Wellbeing; A Cross-sectional Study; *Courtesy of:* Elizabeth A. Molle, PhD, MSN, RN-BC, 2019

Overview of Major Study Findings

Based on a cross-sectional research method with non-purposive quota sampling this study sought to answer four specific research questions. Research procedures and protocol implementation occurred only after receiving necessary human subject use approvals from the county Institutional Review Board and The Catholic University of America Protection of Human Subjects Institutional Review Board. Further, this researcher performed data cleaning and rigorously tested assumptions before analyses. This study enrolled ($N = 116$) community dwelling older adults aged 65 to 84 years old.

Question One

After controlling for age, comorbidities, gender and social desirability, did sedentary behavior influence SWB in older adults? This researcher answered this question with a two–block hierarchical linear multiple regression. Since standard $\log_{10}$ transformations and subsequent square root transformation failed to fix normality distribution problems, this researcher applied bootstrapping. The results found that sedentary behavior significantly influenced SWB after controlling for age, comorbidities, gender and social desirability. Sedentary behavior accounted for 57% of the variance in SWB. The magnitude of the relationship was large, Cohen's $f^2 = 1.44$.

Question Two

After controlling for age, comorbidities, and social desirability, which sedentary behavior estimate (weekday and weekend) explained more of the SWB? This researcher answered this question with a two–block hierarchical linear multiple regression. Since standard $\log_{10}$ transformations and subsequent square root transformation failed to fix normality distribution problems, this researcher applied bootstrapping. The results found that weekend sedentary behavior ($s_r = -0.17$) accounted for more unique variance in SWB than weekday sedentary behavior ($s_r = -0.14$). The effect size was large, Cohen's $f^2 = 1.38$.

Question Three

After controlling for age, comorbidities and social desirability, did gender moderate the relationship between sedentary behavior and SWB? This researcher answered this question with the moderation custom dialog box, PROCESS (model one) in Statistical Package for Social Services (SPSS) software, version 24. The results found that gender did not moderate the relationship between sedentary behavior and SWB. Although, the study found that males spent more time sitting per day ($M = 11.15$ hours/day) compared to females ($M = 10.61$), gender did not significantly interact with sedentary behavior to demonstrate a moderating effect between sedentary behavior and SWB.

Question Four

Did the amount of sedentary behavior relate to differences in stool consistency? This researcher answered this question with a one-way ANOVA. The results found that stool consistency differed based on the amount of sedentary time, Welch $F (2, 40.22) = 32.15, p < 0.001, \omega^2 = 0.53$. Furthermore, post hoc analyses found that statistically significant mean differences in total sedentary behavior occurred among two stool consistency groups: slow colonic time and fast colonic time (M_{diff} = 4.25, 95% BCa CI [2.94, 5.55]) and between normal colonic time and fast colonic time (M_{diff} = 3.54, 95% BCa CI [2.45, 4.59]). This question was intended to be exploratory as prior research does not exist examining sedentary behavior and stool consistency.

These study findings answered four specific research questions that addressed the problem that older adults had high rates of sedentary behavior that influenced their SWB. The next section synthesizes these study findings to prior exemplar research studies.

Findings Synthesized to Exemplar Model Studies

Overview of the Wilson and Cleary Revised Model

The Wilson and Cleary Revised model (WC-R), described in detail in Chapter 1, supported the main study premise that as sedentary behavior increased, SWB decreased. Briefly, the model posited that functional status (i.e., sedentary behavior) influenced general health perceptions (i.e., SWB), (Wilson and Cleary, 1995). A key model assumption posited that individual characteristics (i.e., age, comorbidities, gender social desirability), controlled for in this study, influenced functional status and general health perceptions (Wilson and Cleary, 1995).

Since this study relied heavily on the theoretical underpinnings of the WC-R model, this researcher synthesized the findings from this current study to the three-exemplar studies, described in Chapter 2. These studies were exemplars because they used sophisticated and robust statistical methods to test that a linear relationship existed between functional status and general health perceptions.

The following three exemplars measured functional status differently than this current study, but these prior research studies support the main theoretical underpinning for this study.

Example K: Two-page PhD Dissertation Proposal; Sedentary Behavior and Subjective Wellbeing; A Cross-sectional Study; *Courtesy of*: Elizabeth A. Molle, PhD, MSN, RN-BC, 2019

Background

Sedentary behavior (i.e., sitting, reclining or lying while awake), a distinctly different concept from inactivity (i.e., not meeting physical activity guidelines of 150 minutes exercise/per week) poses an emerging public health concern (Tremblay *et al.*, 2017; World Health Organization, 2010). Sedentary behavior decreases contractions of skeletal muscles and decreases peristalsis thereby increasing colonic transit time, which means that stool takes longer to pass through the colon (Cerdá *et al.* 2016; Engeroff *et al.*, 2017; Lewis & Heaton, 1997).

Biological Plausibility

Sedentary behavior decreases peristalsis, which increases the stools connection time with the mucosal layers of the colon (Cerdá *et al.* 2016; Clark & Mach, 2016) which in turn poses problems because it changes the gut microbiome (Clark & Mach, 2016; Lewis & Heaton, 1997). Gut microbiota influences the efficiency and effectiveness of neurotransmitters, primarily serotonin, which in turn impacts SWB (Cerdá *et al.*, 2016; Monda *et al.*, 2017). This proposed research focuses on how sedentary behavior influences subjective wellbeing (SWB), which remains an understudied consequence of sedentarism.

Problem Statement

High sedentary behavior contributes to multiple problems among community-dwelling older adults. Studies conducted by researchers and epidemiologists provide strong evidence that sedentary behavior poses longer-term problems such as premature mortality and untoward health outcomes even as it generates significant economic costs. However, no research has yet determined if sedentary behavior influences subjective wellbeing (SWB) particularly after controlling for age, gender, comorbidities and social desirability. Evidence supports that higher SWB lowers all-cause mortality and is associated with lower blood pressure, cortisol levels and inflammation (Dierner & Chan, 2011; Sajjad *et al.*, 2017). Evidence suggests that older adults experience higher amounts of sedentary behavior compared to other age groups (Maher *et al.*, 2017; Vallance *et al.*, 2016). While some studies support as age increases, SWB increases (Keyes *et al.*, 2002; Kirkegaard *et al.*, 2017), other evidence supports as age increases, SWB decreases (Braun *et al.*, 2017).

Purpose Statement

This study proposes to determine how sedentary behavior influences

SWB among community dwelling older adults living in the Northeastern United States.

Conceptual Framework

The Wilson and Clearly revised model (WC-R), a middle range theory, provides the theoretical underpinning for this study because it scientifically links functional status (sedentary behavior) to general health perceptions (SWB) and posits that individual characteristics (age, gender, comorbidities, social desirability) influence that relationship thus requiring controlling for their effect. This framework, originally defined in 1995, meets the needs for this study because links abstract subjective patient reported outcomes (Wilson & Cleary, 1995). Strong empirical evidence supports using this model for two reasons. First, studies have tested the link between functional status and general health perceptions. Second, the model has been tested and used in older populations (Gong & Mayo, 2015; Sexton, 2017; Shahrbanian *et al.*, 2016). Example A provides the study schematic.

Research Questions

Question 1

After controlling for age, comorbidities, gender and social desirability, does sedentary behavior influence SWB in older adults?

Question 2

After controlling for age, comorbidities, and social desirability, which of the sedentary behavior estimates (weekday and weekend) explains more of the SWB?

Question 3

After controlling for age, comorbidities and social desirability, does gender moderate the relationship between sedentary behavior and SWB?

Question 4

Is the amount of sedentary behavior related to differences in stool consistency?

Literature Review

Empirical evidence suggests that older adults experience high rates of sedentary behavior ranging from $M = 4.41$ hours/day to $M = 14.21$ hours/day, which equates to approximately sitting 18.3% to 60% of the day (Balboa-Castillo *et al.*, 2011; Ku *et al.*, 2016a). Empirical evidence supports a statistical relationship between sedentary behavior and SWB in adults over 65 (Balboa-Castillo *et al.*, 2011; Bumanv *et al.*, 2010; Ku *et al.*, 2016a; Vallance *et al.*, 2016) and in adults less than 65 years of age (Edwards & Loprinzi, 2017; Hogan *et al.*, 2015). However, few studies have clearly defined sedentary behavior, or measured the SWB construct of hedonic wellbeing (i.e, positive affect) and most studies lacked rigor. Some studies found that older adults experience more weekday sedentary behaviors (Gardner *et al.*, 2014; Maher *et al.*, 2017), while conversely, Vallance *et al.* (2013) found participants experienced higher weekend sedentary rates, but a gap exists as to if those differences impact SWB. Three studies suggest that gender differences exist, with males sitting more hours/day. However, studies failed to test if gender moderates the relationship (Dogra *et al.*, 2017; Espinel *et al.*, 2012; Marshall *et al.*, 2015). Scant evidence supports sedentarism influences colonic transit time, but strong evidence supports that physical activity influences colonic time, which supports the need to answer Question 4 (Cho *et al.*, 2013; Kim *et al.*, 2014). Evidence supports that stool consistency serves as a proxy variable for colonic transit time (Lewis & Heaton, 1997). Evidence further suggests sedentary behavior rates are non-normally distributed (Dogra & Stathokostas, 2014; Ku *et al.*, 2016a, Ku *et al.*, 2016b, Marshall *et al.*, 2015). Lastly, evidence suggests that instrument sequencing causes measurement error when collecting self-reported information about behaviors and attitudes (Polit & Yang, 2016).

Study Design

A cross-sectional stratified quota sampling study design will enable the researcher to determine if: (1) sedentary behavior influences SWB, (2) weekday or weekend sedentary behavior explains more SWB, (3) gender moderates the relationship between sedentary behavior and SWB, and (4) the amount of sedentary behavior influences stool consistency. The *independent variable*, sedentary behavior, refers so the act of sitting, reclining or lying with minimal energy expenditures while awake, as self-reported. The *dependent variable*, SWB, refers to the hedonic part of wellbeing defined as positive emotions, such as joy, happiness and positive affect, as self-reported, by older adults. This study focuses on the hedonic component of SWB because evidence supports it improves with interventions and is more amenable to change (Barley & Lawson, 2016).

Participants: Community-dwelling older adults, ages 65–84.

Sample size: 116 (Example B).

Setting: Three clinical venues within a hospital health system in the Northeastern United States.

Instrumentation: Five valid and reliable instruments (Longitudinal Aging Study Amsterdam Sedentary Behavior Questionnaire, PROMIS® Positive Affect scale, Self-administered Comorbidity Questionnaire, Socially Desirable Response Set, Bristol Stool Form Scale) and a demographic form. Evidence supports that these instruments fit this population. Estimated completion time is 15–20 minutes.

Data Analysis

The researcher will complete data entry twice and check frequency tables for accuracy. After data cleaning and checking logic violations, little MCARs will tests for missing data patterns. Multiple imputation, with 5 iterations, will replace missing data. After univariate, bivariate and reliability tests (Cronbach alpha: LASA, SACQ, SDRS; differential item functioning: PROMIS®) the following tests will answer the above research questions: Question 1 (hierarchical regression); Question 2 (linear regression, bootstrapping: 1000 resamples with replacement; BCa); Question 3 (moderation with PROCESS); Question 4 (one-way ANOVA) using SPSS version 24-software. Example C describes the assumption testing and interpretation plans for these tests. Example D illustrates the bootstrapping stratification, which maintains the quota-sampling plan for gender and location.

Protection of Human Subjects

Permission will be obtained from targeted hospital health system and The Catholic University of America IRBs. Instruments and supplies will be organized to reduce respondent burden. Participants will be contacted before clinic arrival and introduced to the study to allow participants to consider enrolling without undue pressure. If a potential participant opts not to participate in this study, the researcher will log the refusal and record the non-participants gender. This study plans to enroll only participants who agree to participate; participants can change their mind at any time. All data will be secured, coded and saved on a HIPPA compliant hospital computer with encryption software and discarded after 3-years from the date of IRB closure.

Procedure

After inclusion criteria screening, informed consent will be discussed and only interested participants will be enrolled. Participants will complete the instruments in a patient care area unoccupied room to ensure privacy and avoid distractions. Instruments will be stapled to ensure uniformity, instrument administration fidelity and prevent priming effects. The order of instrumentation includes: PROMIS® Positive Affect, demographic, LASA-SBQ, SACQ, SDRS-5 and BSFS. Anticipated completion time is 20 minutes.

Significance

Understanding how sedentary behavior influences SWB may promote public health initiatives that improve health outcomes in older adults. Findings from this study may potentially promote changes to contemporary nursing assessments by incorporating questions related to older adults' sedentary behaviors, and provide evidence to support allocating resources and education for older adults to change sedentary behaviors.

Originality

The literature search did not identify any studies exploring how sedentary behavior influences SWB community dwelling in older adults. The proposed research addresses this and previously noted gaps and aims to offer improved insight into the relationship between sedentary behavior and SWB. Importantly, this study also provides the groundwork for future personalized medicine studies exploring the gut microbiome and the gut-brain axis in sedentary behavior populations.

Example L: Dissertation Abstract; Sedentary Behavior and Subjective Wellbeing; A Cross-sectional Study; *Courtesy of:* **Elizabeth A. Molle, PhD, MSN, RN-BC, 2019**

Sedentary behavior (i.e., sitting, reclining or lying while awake) poses an emerging public health concern due to decreased contractions of skeletal muscles and decreased peristalsis (i.e., increasing colonic transit time) resulting in poor health outcomes (Cerdá *et al.* 2016; Engeroff *et al.*, 2017). High sedentary behavior contributes to multiple problems among community-dwelling older adults.

Statement of the Problem

Prior work by researchers and epidemiologists provides strong evidence that sedentary behavior poses long-term problems such as premature mortality, untoward health outcomes and generates significant economic costs (Biswas *et al.*, 2015; Cerdá *et al.*, 2016; Ding *et al.*, 2016; Monda *et al.*, 2017). Evidence also suggests the presence of one understudied consequence of sedentarism, Subjective Wellbeing (SWB) defined as a complex psychological phenomenon that, in part, includes feelings, emotions and positive thoughts (Diener & Chan, 201, Dogra *et al.*, 2017; Gibson *et al.*, 2017). This study aimed to determine how sedentary behavior influences SWB among community dwelling older adults. The Wilson and Clearly revised model provided the theoretical underpinning for this study; the model component functional status represented sedentary behavior, and the model component, general health perceptions, represented subjective wellbeing. Biological plausibility supports that sedentary behavior decreases peristalsis, which changes gut microbiota and initiates changes to neurotransmitters that affect SWB.

Method

This study utilized a cross-sectional design with stratified quota sampling, by location and gender, to recruit 116 community-dwelling older adults (65–84) who live in the northeastern United States.

Five instruments and a demographic form provided the data collection tools. Two IRBs reviewed and approved the study before commencing to ensure protection of human subjects. Data cleaning, logic violations and Little MCARs test assessed for missing data patterns prior to analyses. This study answered four specific questions.

Results

Question one: after controlling for age, comorbidities, gender and social desirability, did sedentary behavior influence SWB in older adults? The results found that sedentary behavior significantly influences SWB after controlling for age, comorbidities, gender and social desirability. Sedentary behavior added 57% more explanation in the variance. This suggests that sedentary behavior influences SWB. The magnitude of the relationship was large, Cohen's $f^2 = 1.44$. Question two: after controlling for age, comorbidities, and social desirability, which of the sedentary behavior estimates (weekday and weekend) explained more of the SWB? The results found that weekend sedentary behavior ($s_r = -0.17$) explained more SWB than weekday sedentary behavior ($s_r = -0.14$). This suggests that weekend sedentary behavior influences SWB more than weekday sedentary behavior. The effect size was large, Cohen's $f^2 = 1.38$. Question three: after controlling for age, comorbidities and social desirability, did gender moderate the relationship between sedentary behavior and SWB? The results found that gender did not significantly moderate the relationship between sedentary behavior and SWB. Question 4: Was the amount of sedentary behavior related to differences in stool consistency? The results found differences in sedentary behavior among the stool consistency groups, Welch F (2, 40.22) = 32.15, $p < 0.001$, $\omega^2 = .53$. Furthermore, post hoc analyses revealed that statistically significant mean differences in total sedentary behavior occurred between SCT and FST ($M_{diff} = 4.25$, 95% BCa CI [2.94, 5.55]) and between NCT and FCT ($M_{diff} = 3.54$, 95% BCa CI [2.45, 4.59]). This question was intended to provide exploratory information only.

Summary of Conclusions

Prior research from exemplar studies support the main study finding that sedentary behavior influences SWB in older adults. Furthermore, prior research supports this study's finding that older adults experience approximately ten hours per day in sedentary behavior through various domains. Prior research also supports that sedentary behavior differs between weekdays and weekends despite differences in sedentary behavior definitions and measurements which existed among the prior research. Study results suggest multiple implications for clinicians and policymakers, and this researcher identified numerous future research opportunities. In sum, understanding sedentary behavior provides critical information necessary to solve the problem that sedentary behavior influences SWB in community-dwelling older adults.

References

AACN (American Association of Colleges of Nursing). 2015. "The Doctor of Nursing Practice: Current Issues and Clarifying Recommendations." https://www.pncb.org/sites/default/files/2017-02/AACN_DNP_Recommendations.pdf.

AACN (American Association of Colleges of Nursing). 2010. "The Research-Focused Doctoral Program in Nursing: Pathways to Excellence." Washington, DC: https://www.aacnnursing.org/Portals/42/Publications/PhDPosition.pdf.

American Heritage Dictionary of the English Language. 2016. (5th ed.). Boston, MA: Houghton Mifflin Harcourt Publishing Company.

American Psychological Association. 2010. *Publication manual of the American Psychological Association.* (6th ed.). Washington, DC: American Psychological Association.

Ashford University. 2019. Writing a literature review. Retrieved from https://writingcenter.ashford.edu/writing-literature-review

Auerbach, D., et al. 2015. "The DNP by 2015: A Study of the Institutional, Political, and Professional Issues That Facilitate or mpede Establishing a Post-Baccalaureate Doctor of Nursing Practice Program." *Rand Health Quarterly* 5 (1): 3. Accessed Month Day, Year.https://www.ncbi.nlm.nih.gov/pmc/articles/PMC5158236/.

Barnes, T. 2013. *Higher Doctorates in the UK 2013.* Lichfield, England: UK Council for Graduate Education.

Booth, A., Papaioannou, A., and A. Sutton. 2012. *Systematic Approaches to a Successful Literature Review.* London: Sage Publishing, Inc.

Cook, K.E. and Murowchick, E. 2014. "Do literature review skills transfer from one course to another?" *Psychology Learning and Teaching 13* (1): 3–11. Retrieved from http://dx.doi.org/10.2304/plat.2014.13.1.3

Concordia University. 2019. "How to write a literature review." Retrieved from https://library.concordia.ca/help/writing/literature-review.php

DeLuca, C. M. 2019. "Diabetes interventions for Hispanic adults." Capstone Project Paper. Unpublished manuscript. The Catholic University of America School of Nursing. Washington, D.C.

Froese, A. D., Gantz, B. S., and Henry, B. S. 1998. "Teaching students to write literature reviews: A metaanalytic model." *Teaching of Psychology, 25* (2), 102–105. Retrieved from http://dx.doi.org/10.1207/s15328023top2502_4

George Mason University. 2019. "Writing an Abstract." Retrieved from https://writingcenter.gmu.edu/guides/writing-an-abstract.

Goodman, P., Robert, R. C. & Johnson, J.E. (2020). Rigor in PhD dissertation research. *Nursing Forum.* 1-10. https://doi.org/10.1111/nuf.12477

Gust, K. J. 2006. "Teaching with Tiffany's: A 'go-lightly' approach to information literacy instruction for adults and senior learners." *Reference Services Review, 34* (4), 557–569. Retrieved from https://doi.org/10.1108/00907320610716440

Hendry, G., Armstrong, S. and Bromberger, N. 2012. "Implementing standards-based assessment effectively: Incorporating discussion of exemplars into classroom teaching." *Assessment & Evaluation in Higher Education 37* (2): 149–161.

Kennedy, D. 2019. "What is a dissertation?" *Royal Literary Fund.* Retrieved from https://www.rlf.org.uk/resources/what-is-a-dissertation-how-is-it-different-from-an-essay/

Lee, C. 2015. "Contractions in formal writing: What's allowed, what's not." *The APA Style Blog.* Retrieved from https://blog.apastyle.org/apastyle/2015/12/contractions-in-formal-writing-whats-allowed-whats-not.html

Lyons, B. P. and Elmedni, B. 2015. "Writing skills development for graduate students: Workshop intervention using a student-centered learning approach." *Journal of Education and Social Policy 2* (1): 38–49.

Machi, L.A. and McEvoy, B. T. 2012. *The literature review: Six steps to success.* (2nd ed.). Thousand Oaks, CA: Corwin Press.

Martin, D. L., Brewer, M.K., and Barr, N. 2011. "Gradually guiding nursing students through their capstone course: Registered nurse preceptors share their experiences." *Nursing Research and Practice*, 645125: 1–6. Retrieved from http://dx.doi.org/10.1155/2011/645125

McCall, R.C., Padron. K., and Andrews, C. 2018. "Evidence-based instructional strategies for adult learners: A review of the literature." *Codex (2150-086X)*, *4* (4), 29–47.Retrieved from https://academicworks.cuny.edu/cgi/viewcontent.cgi?article=1048&context=bx_pubs

Melnyk, B.M., Fineout-Overholt, E. 2019. *Evidence-based practice in nursing & healthcare: A guide to best practice (4th ed.).* Philadelphia: Lippincott Williams and Wilkins.

Molle, E. A. 2019. "Sedentary behavior and subjective wellbeing: A cross-sectional study." Doctoral Dissertation. Unpublished manuscript. The Catholic University of America School of Nursing. Washington, D.C.

National Institutes of Health, Office of Extramural Research. 2018. *Enhancing rigor and transparency.* Retrieved from https://grants.nih.gov/policy/reproducibility/index.htm

National Organization of Nurse Practitioner Faculties. 2013. *Titling of the Doctor of Nursing Practice Project.* Retrieved from: https://cdn.ymaws.com/www.nonpf.org/resource/resmgr/dnp/dnpprojectstitlingpaperjune

Noble, K. A. (1994). *Changing doctoral degrees: An international perspective.* Buckingham, UK: Society for Research into Higher Education and Open University Press.

Nordquist, R. 2019. Definition and examples of jargon. *ThoughtCo.* Retrieved from https://www.thoughtco.com/what-is-jargon-16912022.pdf

Pautasso, M. 2013. Ten simple rules for writing a literature review. *PLoS Comput Biol 9* (7): e1003149. Retrieved from https://doi.org/10.1371/journal.pcbi.1003149

Poling, K. 2008/2009. Writing a history paper: Formulating a research question. Cambridge, MA: Harvard University. Retrieved from https://history.fas.harvard.edu/files/history/files/research_question.pdf?m=1459176775

Pratt, D.D. 1988. Andragogy as a relational construct. *Adult Education Quarterly, 38* (3): 160–181.

Rapchak, M. E., Lewis, L. A., Motyka, J. K., and Balmert, M. 2015. Information literacy and adult learners: Using authentic assessment to determine skill gaps. *Adult Learning, 26*(4), 135–142. Retrieved from https://doi.org/10.1177%2F1045159515594155

Rempel, H.G., and Davidson, J. 2008. Providing information literacy instruction to graduate students through literature review workshops. *Issues in Science and Technology Librarianship. 53.* Retrieved from https://core.ac.uk/download/pdf/37766536.pdf.

Riesenberg, L.A and Justice, E.M. 2014. Conducting a successful systematic review of the literature, Part 1. *Nursing 2014, 44*(4), 13–17.

Rosenberg, R.P. (1961. The first American doctor of philosophy degree: A centennial salute to Yale, 1861–1961". *Journal of Higher Education. 32* (7): 387–394. Retrieved from https://www.jstor.org/stable/1978076

Rudestam, K. E., and Newton, R. R. 2007. Surviving your dissertation: A comprehensive guide to content and process (3rd ed.). Thousand Oaks, CA, USA: Sage Publications, Inc.

Sadler, D. R. 2010. Beyond feedback: Developing student capability in complex appraisal. *Assessment & Evaluation in Higher Education 35* (5): 535–550.

Sovacool, B. K., Axsen, J., and Sorrella, S. 2018. Promoting novelty, rigor, and style in energy social science: Towards codes of practice for appropriate methods and research design. *Energy Research & Social Science, 4,* 12–42. Retrieved from https://doi.org/10.1016/j.erss.2018.07.007

The Catholic University of America. 2019. DNP scholarly project format. Unpublished manuscript.

To, J. and Carliss, D. 2015. Making productive use of exemplars: Peer discussion and teacher guidance for positive transfer of strategies. *Journal of Further and Higher Education 40* (6): 746–764. Retrieved from http://dx.doi.org/10.1080/0309877X.2015.1014317

Want, D.R. 2019. Identification of Primary Care Nurse Practitioner Procedural Skills Used in Practice. DNP Scholarly Project. Unpublished manuscript. The Catholic University of America School of Nursing. Washington, D.C.

Wiles, E. 2019. Best Evidence-Based Interventions to Improve Appointment Adherence in Adult Multiple Sclerosis Patients. Capstone Project Paper. Unpublished manuscript. The Catholic University of America School of Nursing. Washington, D.C.

SECTION III

The Messy Writing Process

I'm not a very good writer, but I'm an excellent re-writer.
—James Michener

Introduction

NO matter the vantage point, writing is a process, and a messy one at that—filled with multiple drafts, revisions, and edits. Writing requires discipline and a commitment to engaging in a series of steps that every writer journeys through each time they develop a manuscript (Irvin 2010). Novice writers, such as new nursing students in graduate school, tend to think of a writing product as a singular course assignment instead of stages that require multiple drafts and revisions (Johnson and Rulo 2019; Ashby 2005). Bypassing these essential stages usually occurs when student writers binge write or develop a writing assignment hours before its due date (Brookshire and Brundage 2016). The result is usually a poorly written product and a low assignment grade. Writers who appreciate and engage in the writing process, especially the revision process, quickly learn the power of composing and revising in elevating the quality of their writing (Rulo 2019; Life Rich Publishers n.d.; Derntl 2014).

The Stages of Writing

The process of writing primarily involves three stages: pre-writing, drafting, and revision (Johnson and Rulo 2019), although some authors offer a fourth important step: editing (Luke 2018; Egerton 2019). Figure 5.1 illustrates the process that every author invariably travels through when creating a manuscript (Johnson and Rulo 2019, 59).

Pre-writing	Drafting	Revision
• Planning • Generating content • Organizing	• Fleshing out ideas • Creating your first draft	• Re-conceiving • Scrubbing • Creating new draft

Figure 5.1. The Traditional Stages of Writing. Source: Johnson and Rulo 2019 (This article was published in the Journal of Professional Nursing 35(1), Johnson, J.E. & Rulo,K., Problems in the profession: How and why writing skills must be improved, p.59, Copyright Elsevier, 2019).

Pre-Writing

Pre-writing allows authors to formulate ideas, generate concepts, and clarify terms that the writer envisions using in the narrative. Pre-writing provides a record of ideas for use in the first draft (Otis College n.d., 2). This list enables the writer to list the relevant topics, and then refine the list and create better ideas (Berkowitz 2004). An improved list helps to keep the writer organized, and increases the likelihood of a logically-organized, coherent document.

There are four general approaches to pre-writing. One involves *brainstorming*, which is an effective way to generate ideas for a narrative (Otis College n.d.; Hale n.d.). This approach requires the author to write down phrases, ideas, or topics without editing or eliminating any possible ideas. The intent is to develop a long list of possibilities. The next step is grouping the phrases, words, and concepts and then labeling these groups from which the writer can develop the narrative. Developing one sentence for each group can provide potential topic sentences in creating the narrative sections and subsections.

Another popular technique is *free writing*, a somewhat intense process that requires the author to write quickly and non-stop for a pre-set period of time (Kentucky University 2019; Otis College n.d.; Luke 2018). The process does not allow editing and is useful when an idea seems out of reach. After the time period ends, the writer reviews the material and circles the most interesting or prominent ideas. The process is repeated until the focus is sufficiently narrowed and final topics emerge.

Looping is similar to free writing in that the writer focuses for a shorter time on free writing, then loops to the written material for five to ten minutes further refining and narrowing thoughts and ideas (Kentucky University 2019). This continues until an improved idea emerges.

Listing is another method that produces a lot of information in a short period of time. Listing is particularly useful in projects that begin at a very broad level and must be trimmed by creating associations that generate more detail (Kentucky University 2019). This pre-writing process requires the writer to write down every possible term that relates to the broad topic. The terms are grouped and labeled. At this point, the author writes a sentence about each label effectively creating a topic sentence or a thesis statement (Kentucky University 2019).

Finally, an author must address the *What—So What?* conundrum as part of the pre-writing stage (University of North Carolina n.d.; Derntl 2014). The writer first identifies the topic area of interest—the *What*—by listing phrases and sentences that relate or describe the topic. Then, the writer reads that material and answers the question *So What?*—why are these elements and the topic worthy of developing a narrative? Are there other content areas that are more important or that enhance the topic? Focusing on the *What—So What?* early in the writing process can save the writer from multiple revisions as the drafting process unfolds.

The pre-writing process includes the planning phase of writing, generates content, and provides an organization—a road map—for the manuscript. If completed properly, the author will remain on track for developing a narrative with a logical flow of ideas.

Figure 5.2. The Drafting Journey. Source: Johnson and Rulo 2019 (This article was published in the Journal of Professional Nursing 35(1), Johnson, J.E. & Rulo, K., Problems in the profession: How and why writing skills must be improved, p.59, Copyright Elsevier, 2019).

Drafting

After engaging in pre-writing, the author is ready to begin drafting the document. However, the road to and through the drafting journey can test even the best writers. Figure 5.2 illustrates the myriad of steps a writer *should* travel to arrive at a first draft of a document (Johnson and Rulo 2019).

Developing the first draft begins with developing one sentence or short paragraph that summarizes the intent of the document (Capella University n.d.). In doing so, the author highlights the main idea, key terms, and envisioned concepts that will become the evidence the writer will use to support the main idea. Consider the following example:

> DNP programs across the country have transformed traditional PhD education for nurses from a research-based focus to a practice focus that emphasizes innovation in complex healthcare institutions. While innovation in the healthcare industry has advanced clinical patient care, many consider the pace too slow and note the absence of the nursing profession in leading serious care delivery change. Envisioned innovations include the development of technology that enables patient access to care from afar though telehealth technology, care delivery model transformation that focuses on improved efficiency, and cost reduction, and improvements in clinical outcomes for patients regardless of clinical program or venue.

Using a scholarly tone, the writer described an issue in this brief paragraph, presented a solution and identified the potential benefits. Given the clarity of direction, the reader can predict narrative sections and subsections. For instance:

- Transformation of doctoral education for nurses as a catalyst for innovation.
- Innovation in healthcare intended to drive improvements in clinical patient care.
- The pace of innovation suggests an historical slow growth that fails to support improvements required today and in the future.
- Nursing's lack of leadership in developing innovative approaches to a series of aspects in the delivery of healthcare is evidenced and must be rectified.
- Envisioned innovations that rank important include telehealth, care delivery model transformation, and improvement in clinical outcomes.

This example underscores the importance of three concepts in the drafting stage. First, the main idea relates to the reader the author's position on the topic. Second, the text alerts readers who differ with the author's viewpoint to entertain the topic from a different vantage point. Third, the author provides evidence that supports the main idea.

As a writer addresses each component, the writer may realize that the original problem statement lacks credibility from an absence of evidence or perhaps the content lacks sufficient detail. Revising the document's intent or purpose statement is part of the drafting process and illustrates the creative nature of the writing process.

Creating an Outline

The next step in the drafting stage includes *creating an outline* for the manuscript and identifying sections and subsections that the author plans to address as the document evolves. This outline enables the listing, looping, and free writing ideas to become organized into a coherent, logical sequence that demonstrates relationships between ideas (Luke 2018). Most importantly, an outline keeps the writer focused on the essence of the manuscript and not on tangents. After an outline is completed, the writer is ready to create an initial draft of the document.

Developing the Narrative

In the drafting stage, the author introduces the main idea of the narrative, followed by well-developed supportive arguments based on evidence (Capella University n.d.) Most students in graduate programs as well as journal authors write about familiar material, in which they may be a subject matter expert. A well-developed outline enables those writers to create a solid initial draft more easily if they remain within the construct of the outline. The value of developing an outline applies equally for short written assignments as well as major manuscripts. An outline assures that the document will flow logically and increases the opportunity that the topic will be developed with clarity.

Writing the Introduction

The introduction may present writers with a unique challenge (Freese 2013; The Catholic University of America n.d.). Writers sometime struggle with the degree to which they should include general or specific content to define the topic, or whether the tone fits the narrative sufficiently to interest the reader. As a result, many writers write the introduction last, after the middle portion of the document nears completion (Capella University n.d.). Keeping these components in mind may prove helpful:

- Introduce the purpose of the manuscript
- Orient the reader to how the paper is organized
- Offer evidence that supports the importance of the main topic
- Use a scholarly tone and evidence to interest the reader.

Using Sources for Evidence

Source selection can add or detract from a manuscript's credibility. Primary sources contain original information from an author, while secondary sources are interpretations of facts presented by the primary author. Using primary sources strengthens credibility. Always state your position in your own words and then cite the source as you write. Avoid overuse of quotes. Simply make your point and cite your source. In more extensive projects, however, such as in a literature review for a dissertation, the writer provides extensive details about the works of primary authors. All authors must avoid plagiarism. Since inadvertent plagiarism can easily occur, it is always wise to use a plagiarism checker such as Turnitin or SafeAssign, which can identify can assist suspicious content that may be plagiarized.

Logical Flow

Academicians and prolific readers may refer to a manuscript as a "good read," which suggests enjoyment of reading a well-written manuscript (Williams and Bizup 2017). But how do you create a clear and cohesive manuscript that flows? One suggestion requires the writer to continually relate one idea to another in addressing the myriad of topics comprising a document. The aim is to move the reader from discussion to discussion *seamlessly* without interruption or get-the-reader-to-the-front-door-of-the-next-discussion-without-knowing-how-they-arrived. Here are some suggestions from Capella University (n.d. 25) to develop a good read:

- Repetition
  - —Refer to key words and phrases repeatedly signaling to the reader their importance
  - —Repeat for emphasis
  - —Use consistent words and phraseology
  - —Remember, repletion "appeals to the ear" and makes writing "seem to flow"
  - —Repetition "weaves" content from different paragraphs together like a strand of thread that reinforces manuscript content.
  - —Example:
    - – The pace of *innovation* in healthcare has failed to keep with the transformations required to enable successful healthcare reform.
    - – Telehealth, a promising *innovation* currently in the early stages of development, may eventually improve access-to-care for millions of Americans who struggle to find providers who can diagnosis and treat medical conditions.
    - – The transformation of care delivery models and improvement in clinical outcomes hold promise as *innovations* that could be advanced by expert nurses with DNP degrees.
- In moving from idea to idea, tell the reader what you plan to address. Then, address it.
- Clarify the stages of the argument or discussion you present. For example, *initially, continuing, finally* and *first, second, third, etc.* orients readers to the discussion strategy.
- Using words that link thoughts together can tie sentences and paragraphs *creating a tight and comfortable* "flow". Examples include: *however, therefore*, and *consequently*.

Writing the Conclusion

A good conclusion reminds the reader of the most important, cogent points of the manuscript. The narrative should highlight those topics that the writer finds most relevant. Include in this section the solution to the initial problem presented at the outset, describe the impact of that problem, identify the needed action to address it, and relate or synthesize the main topic to other relevant literature or subjects (The Catholic University of America n.d.; Capella University n.d.).

Never offer new ideas in the conclusion. This confuses the reader and suggests that the writer failed to address an important aspect in the manuscript. If the new idea is important, then the writer must revise the manuscript. Finally, at this point, it may be more fruitful to develop the introduction since the writer will have fully developed the discussion.

As the drafting stage of the writing process concludes, one key aspect in draft development is avoiding the urge to proofread and edit as the draft unfolds. The interruption this causes in thinking and focus diminishes the narrative development and can easily distract the writer. One should deal with one task—developing the document. Remember that the intent of drafting is to flesh out ideas (Johnson and Rulo 2019) and create a draft document worthy of the next step in the messy writing process: revision.

Revise, Revise, Revise

Prior to beginning the revision stage, the author should take a break from the manuscript for at least twenty-four to forty-eight hours. This enables the writer to view their work from a more objective perspective (Johnson and Rulo 2019; Ashby 2005). The revising process commences with the assessment of word choice, organization, logical flow, the presence of sufficient evidence, and scholarly tone (University of North Carolina n.d.). Effectively, the writer reviews their entire work as critically as possible in order to reword, cut, reorganize, and delete or expand content. Keep in mind that writers write to *explain* so that readers can *learn* (Egerton 2019). The process is a repetitive, and aims to develop a manuscript worthy of graduate program level writing and/ or potential publication in a professional journal.

An initial step in the revision process is to address logical flow, and larger issues such as the argument the writer intends to advance and the organization and structure of the manuscript (Berkowitz 2004; Capella University n.d.). This is the most important part of the revision stage. Addressing these areas first makes the writing process more efficient (Johnson and Rulo 2019). Initially, the writer must refrain from scrubbing or focusing on sentence structure, word choice, and grammatical errors. After the structure is clear, strong, and logical, the author can engage in a robust effort to polish prose can effectively take place.

Table 5.1 illustrates the myriad of steps embedded in the revision stage (Johnson and Rulo 2019; Rulo 2019; Duistermaat n.d.)

TABLE 5.1. *Steps and Considerations in Revising Manuscripts.*

1. Objectively view the manuscript.
2. Prepare to reorganize and/or expand content.
3. Consider the audience, the style, tone, logical flow and clarity.
   a. Answer the question: *Does this manuscript address the needs of readers and any larger audience?*
   b. Does the writing style fulfill course or journal requirements?
   c. Is a scholarly tone evident?
   d. Does the content logically flow?
   e. Is the discussion and content clear and concise?
4. Determine if the argument is sufficiently supported by primary source evidence.
5. After reading the draft, would readers be able to
   a. State the purpose of the document?
   b. Identify the four most important points of the narrative?
   c. Offer evidence supporting each key point?
6. Review each paragraph individually assuring that only one topic is discussed at a time.
   a. Is the content accurate?
   b. Is the depth of content sufficient or too much?
7. Are descriptions, definitions, examples helpful and clearly presented?
8. Would creating tables, adding Figures or diagrams enhance the presentation of content?
9. Do gaps in the discussion of content exist? Does it interrupt flow and diminish clarity?
10. Does the flow reflect logical sequencing? Do key thoughts follow each other logically? Do stray thoughts need removal? Are important ideas missing? Do headings guide the reader sufficiently?
11. Are transition words such as *however, moreover, first, second, third* tread sentences and paragraphs as well as sections together?

Adapted from: Johnson and Rulo 2019; Duistermaat n.d.; The Catholic University of America n.d.

Writing to "Express" vs. "Impress"

Many writers, particularly those in academic settings and novice writers, are concerned about writing with a sophisticated, professional tone (Capella University n.d.). In the effort to achieve a scholarly tone, such writers may develop a style that is exceptionally formal and complex. Instead of aiming to impress, it is better to aim to express.

Consider the following examples:

- *Writing to Impress:* Creating technological super-structures for buttressing complex healthcare industry information and ameliorating inter-operativity circumstances only serves to worsen the increasingly fragile financial algorithm that underpins this significant portion of the U.S. economy.

- *Writing to Express:* Developing technology that can advance IT connectivity for all healthcare providers may result in an unstainable financial burden for the US economy.

Writers must aim to find a balance between developing a sophisticated scholarly tone and writing with clarity for the immediate reader and the broader unintended audience. Simplifying sentence structure and word choice can contribute to establishing a suitable balance.

Editing: The "4th" Stage of the Writing Process

Scrubbing or *polishing* consists of editing and proofreading (Johnson and Rulo 2019) and can be accomplished in a variety of ways. The goal is smoothing the rough edges of the draft prior to completion. In this stage, writers continue to assess tone, style, flow, and rhythm to achieve clarity and conciseness, which are reflected in the author's choice and arrangement of words, phrases, and sentences. Remember that word choice refers to diction and clarity that creates the style and rhythm of the document. Tone refers to mood or attitude resulting from word choice, sentence structure, and length (Ong 2014). Style mirrors the writer's attitude and enables the reader to appreciate personality expressed in the sentence and paragraph rhythm and logical flow.

Perhaps the activity most associated with editing is *proofreading*, which is the final review to correct technical errors or flaws in spelling, grammar, and punctuation. Given the spellcheck function in most word processing programs, spelling mistakes are often difficult to catch because the spell check function automatically replaces misspelled words. In many instances, homophones (same sound, different spelling) remain in the document. Grammar is another proofreading activity that addresses the contemporary use of grammar rules such as syntax and inflection (Capella University n.d.). Finally, correct punctuation including the use of characters or symbols (commas, question marks) instructs the reader to read the sentence as the writer intended. Therefore, proofreading for correct punctuation is an important aspect of this final fourth stage.

One of the easiest, most effective way to begin the proofreading process is reading the document aloud. This practice helps the writer to "clarify meaning, perfect rhythm and spot errors" (Johnson and Rulo

2019, 59). An additional useful practice is having another person read the document for clarity, form, sequencing, and logic. Another's viewpoint brings the element of objectivity from the reader "who does not know" to the writer "who knows" or is the subject matter expert. One final suggestion is to engage in revising using a *sentence-by-sentence method* that focuses on reducing sentence length, improving word choice, and tightening sentence structure (Duistermaat n.d.; Ong 2014). Table 5.2 offers a series of editing methods that may contribute to im-

TABLE 5.2. Selected Components of the Editing Process.

1. Eliminate meaningless words
   Example:
      Actually, addressing technology improvements specifically depend on DNP-prepared nurse interest and leadership than on any kind of technology enhancement.
   Edited:
      Technology improvements depend more on DNP-prepared nurse interest and leadership than on technology.
2. Delete repetitive words
   Example:
      In developing effective intra-operable IT systems, vendors must first and foremost address user-friendliness of their products.
   Edited:
      In developing effective intra-operable IT systems, vendors must address user-friendliness of their products.
3. Use strong descriptive words—especially verbs
   Example:
      Nurses prepared at the doctoral level have got to emerge as key leaders in the transformation of the healthcare industry.
   Edited:
      Nurses prepared at the doctoral level stand to emerge as key leaders in the transformation of the healthcare industry.
4. Remember the acronym F.A.N.B.O.Y.S. for the seven coordinating words that require a comma before joining two sentences together: for, and, nor, but, or, yet, so
   Example:
      Intra-operable IT systems represent an important component of transforming the healthcare industry, but without a robust academic focus on informatics nurses prepared at the doctoral level may struggle when participating in system design discussions.
5. Read the document backwards after one round of editing by slowly assessing each sentence. Check for mechanical errors such as colons and commas.
6. Look for unclear, particularly long sentences and mark for revision. This helps to eliminate run-on sentences, adds an opportunity for improved clarity, and allows for enhanced logical content flow.
7. Assure adherence to required format guidelines such as APA, MLA, etc.

Adapted from: Capella University 2019; The Catholic University of America n.d.; Atwood 2016.

proving efficiency during the editing stage (Capella University 2019; The Catholic University of America n.d.; Atwood 2016).

Final proofreading requires writers to check for accuracy of formatting specifics such as headings, spacing, numbering and appendices. Many writers find that by reading the manuscript backwards, errors are more easily identified and corrected, while reading aloud is helpful as well (Berkowitz 2004; Johnson and Rulo 2019; The Catholic University of America n.d.).

The writing process reflects a series of stages that require serious writer engagement and focus. Eliminating or failing to focus on any of the stages usually ends in a document that needs significant revision and a manuscript development process that is overly tedious. This chapter assisted novice authors to quickly learn what experienced authors know: the pre-writing phase is important, and the work completed in this phase drives success during the drafting of documents. Further, the content underscored that seasoned authors welcome multiple revisions and the opportunity to improve drafts because a solid draft results in a smoother, less intense editing process. There is no substitute for the hard work a writer must invest in each stage of writing. With practice, each writing project becomes better organized and easier to develop, and this results in a quality scholarly manuscript that is suitable for academic dissemination or journal publication.

Practice Exercises

Questions to refresh content discussion:

1. Steps in the writing process include: (A) drafting, (B) pre-writing, (C) editing, and (D) revising. Which is the correct sequence?
   a. D, B, A, E
   b. B, C, D, A
   c. A, B, C, D
   d. B, A, D, C

2. In the pre-writing stage, you most likely would:
   a. List every conceivable idea or thought about a topic.
   b. Research literature to find evidence about a topic.
   c. Develop full sentences for each idea you generate.
   d. Edit your phrases and words as you list them.

3. How would best describe the pre-writing process:
   a. Intense
   b. Structured
   c. Leisure
   d. Informal

4. Which one of these activities is included in developing a draft?
   a. Correcting weak verb use
   b. Writing full sentences
   c. Exploring an interesting avenue
   d. Looping ideas

5. Developing an outline increases the writer's chance to:
   a. Decide how to modify section content
   b. Narrow the manuscript's topic
   c. Produce a logically-sequenced and clear narrative
   d. Avoid plagiarism

6. A most important component of the drafting process is:
   a. Correcting for grammatical errors
   b. Addressing the *What-So What?*
   c. Proceed in an orderly fashion
   d. Change words to interest readers

7. In developing the Introduction, the writer should aim to:
   a. Hook the reader
   b. Address every component envisioned in the narrative
   c. Cite primary sources
   d. Support offered ideas with evidence

8. In developing the Conclusion, the writer should aim to:
   a. Address every element in the document
   b. Highlight those topics that the writer finds most relevant
   c. Identify new, interesting aspects of the topic
   d. Include only the content contained in the introduction.

9. In determining the strength of a first draft, the writer might:
   a. Share the draft with a colleague for feedback
   b. Read the draft aloud
   c. Discuss key terms with subject matter experts
   d. Analyze the draft from a sentence level for clarity and flow
   e. All of these

10. What is the result of failing to carefully proofread?
    a. Grammatical errors may remain in the document.
    b. The document many contain unnecessary words.
    c. The reader may become distracted.
    d. The graduate student receives a low grade and/or a publisher rejection.
    e. All of these

Correct answers:

1. d
2. a
3. d
4. b
5. c
6. b
7. a
8. a
9. e
10. e

Edit the Following Document

The procedure of conducting research at the institution of University of Belgium starts with ascertaining whether the research requires an IRB or not. All proposals that involve human subjects have to have a tumultuous IRB approval, in addition, special protections granted to minors, prisoners, pregnant women and vulnerable populations. The Principal investigator (PI) completes a rigorous ethics certification course online. Considering the sensitivity of the information collected. The instructor can require if they want to that students complete the CITI (collaborative institutional training initiative), an online course, conjoined to the IRB application and renewed once a semester until the research is completed, whichever comes first.

The PI and students must complete an electronic application which takes about 4 weeks to get a response back. The IRB application goes to the OHRP, the Office of Human Research Protections, who oversees the ethical and legal requirements concerning human subjects. The application also goes to the IRB chair, the director, ORI (office of research investigation), and economic development. The IRB chair and staff review the application and the IRB comprises five members from diverse backgrounds. The IRB ascertains the acceptability of proposed research in terms of institution policies and regulations, applicable laws, and standards of professional conduct and practices. The IRB follows federal guidelines, in addition to the rules applied by the country of Belgium. IRB follows the institutional policy purports protection of human participants in research, and IRB Standards Operating Procedures (SOP's).

The IRB protocol can follow all four avenues, i.e. full board review, expedited review, non-human, and exempt from review. The full board review consists of elevated levels of risk, with highly sensitive information and methodology; this one takes the longest for the IRB to review, i.e. 4–6 weeks. The expedited review pertains to lower risk levels and not to time constraints. The chair determines the level of review. Once the IRB reviews the application, the decision gets sent to the principal investigator (PI), as approved or not approved. As you can see, it is a very convoluted and tedious process.

References

Atwood, B. 2016. "Self-Editing Basics: 10 Simple Ways to Edit Your Own Book." https://thewritelife.com/self-editing-basics/.

Ashby, M. 2005. *How to Write A Paper.* (6th ed). Cambridgeshire, England: University of Cambridge. http://www-mech.eng.cam.ac.uk/mmd/ashby-paper-V6.pdf.

Berkowitz, D. 2004. *Five Steps to Writing an Essay.* Pittsburgh, PA, USA: University of Pittsburgh. http://www.pitt.edu/~dmberk/writing05.pdf.

Brookshire, R. H., and S. B. Brundage. 2017. *Writing Scientific Research in Communication Sciences and Disorders.* San Diego, CA, USA: Plural Publishing.

Burnell, C., J. Wood, M. Babin, S. Pesznecker, and N. Rosevear. n.d.. "The Word on College Reading and Writing." https://openoregon.pressbooks.pub/wrd/chapter/writing-a-first-draft/.

Capella University n.d.. *The Writing Process.* Minneapolis, MN, USA: Capella University. http://www.capella.edu/interactivemedia/onlineWritingCenter/downloads/TheWritingProcess.pdf.

Colorado State University. n.d. *Writing the Research Paper.* Retrieved from https://writing.colostate.edu/textbooks/informedwriter/chapter10.pdf

Dernti, M. 2014. "Basics of research paper writing and publishing." *International Journal of Technology Enhanced Learning, 6* (2), 105–123. Retrieved from https://dbis.rwth-aachen.de/~derntl/papers/misc/paperwriting.pdf

Duistermaat, H. n.d.. "How to put your thoughts into words: 3 proven strategies." Retrieved from https://www.enchantingmarketing.com/writing-strategies/

Egerton, K. 2019. "The Writing Process." Retrieved from https://my.nps.edu/documen ts/111693070/112854069/2019.07.16-3+Foundations+-+The+Writing+Process+% 5BEgerton%5D.pdf/e72f07b5-f2b6-4433-905c-6aaf1c733aa4

Freese, C. 2013. "Fruitless first draft struggles." Retrieved from https://www.writersdi gest.com/editor-blogs/there-are-no-rules/fruitless-first-draft-struggles

Hale, A. n.d.. "The writing process." Retrieved from https://www.dailywritingtips.com/ the-writing-process/

Irvin, L. L. 2010. "What is academic writing?" *Writing spaces: Readings on writing,* (1). Retrieved from https://wac.colostate.edu/books/writingspaces1/irvin--what-is-academic-writing.pdf

Johnson, J. E., and K. Rulo. 2019. "Problems in the Profession: How and Why Writing Skills Must Be Improved." *Journal of Professional Nursing,* 35(1), 57–64. Kansas University. 2019. "Prewriting Strategies." Retrieved from http://writing.ku.edu/ thesis-statements

Life Rich Publishers. n.d.. "The 5-step writing process: From brainstorming to publishing." Retrieved from https://www.liferichpublishing.com/AuthorResources/ General/5-Step-Writing-Process.aspx

Luke, A. 2018. "The four essential stages of writing (for anything you're working on)." Retrieved from www.aliventures.com/essential-writing-stages

Ong, C. 2014. *The process approach to writing remediation.* Edgbaston, Birmingham, UK:University of Birmingham. Retrieved from https://www.birmingham.ac.uk/ Documents/college-artslaw/cels/essays/languageteaching/Ong%20M5%20(Dist). pdf

Otis College. n.d.. "Prewriting strategies." Retrieved from https://otis.libguides.com/c. php?g=705076&p=5007402

Rulo, K. 2019. "Disseminating knowledge through mastering writing competency." *The DNP Nurse in Executive Leadership Roles.* Lancaster, PA: DEStech Publications, Inc.

Study Guides and Strategies. n.d. "Rough drafts." Retrieved from https://www.studygs. net/writing/roughdrafts.htm

The Catholic University of America. n.d. "Writing Center handouts." Retrieved from https://success.catholic.edu/academic-support/writing-center/handouts.html

University of Kansas Writing Center. 2019. "Pre-writing strategies." Retrieved from http://writing.ku.edu/prewriting-strategies

University of North Carolina. n.d. "In-class writing exercises." Retrieved from https:// writingcenter.unc.edu/faculty-resources/tips-on-teaching-writing/in-class-writing-exercises/

Williams, J. M. and Bizup, J. 2017. *Style: Lessons in clarity and grace.* (12th ed.). Upper Saddle River, NJ: Pearson Education, Inc.

CHAPTER 6

Writing a Lot

You can't wait for inspiration. You have to go after it with a club.
—Jack London

Writer's Block

WRITER'S block can seem a bit like the Bermuda Triangle—many people swear that it exists, that there would be no explanation for myriad phenomena otherwise, while others dismiss it as mere myth. Fantasy novelist Terry Pratchett once remarked that "There's no such thing as writer's block. That was invented by people in California who couldn't write" (Hult 2016, 330). And yet, haven't we all had the experience of staring blankly at a similarly blank computer screen, waiting for something, some spark of inspiration to set our fingers typing? And while it may or may not fit many definitions of writer's block, the phenomenon of "writing apprehension"—which describes the situation in which "anxiety about writing outweighs the projection of gain from writing" (Daiker 1989/1999, 155)—is very real indeed and can be debilitating for those affected (Daly and Miller 1975; Pajares and Johnson 1994; Pajares 2003). Call it what you will, the disinclination or the inability to write is one of the preeminent problems that writers experience at one time or another. It happens to every writer at some point, and for some it is a regular part of their writing lives. The real pressing question is, what can we do about it?

Unfortunately, there is no magic formula that will solve our problems with writing productivity. Writing takes hard work, but just as important, it takes a regimen of regular practice. The American historian and philosopher Will Durant (1930) once creatively paraphrased Aristotle in saying that "we are what we repeatedly do. Excellence, then, is not an act but a habit" (87). The key to writing a lot, and to achieving success in your writing projects (including the success of actually completing them), lies in the habits that you foster, the daily routines and rituals, and the forethought you put into making your work do the best work for you. Sadly, you won't be able to "binge write" your way through graduate school and the profession (Brookshire and Brundage 2016). Maybe you could get away with pulling all-nighters as an undergraduate, but that isn't how professional scholars produce their work. So, how do they? In this chapter, we will discuss the habits and behaviors that professional writers and researchers employ to ensure high levels of writing productivity. Making use of the habits and practices outlined in this chapter will not mean that you will never struggle again as a writer, and that you will always be productive every time you sit down to write. Sadly, we can't and don't promise that. It will mean, however, that you will have fewer struggles and will be well-equipped to weather the adversity that comes with those difficult moments of writing apathy and failure.

The Importance of Planning: A Cautionary Excursion

You may be familiar with the Greek myth that tells the stories of two brothers, the Titans Prometheus and Epimetheus. The two are an antithetical pair. Prometheus's name means "forethought," while Epimetheus's name means "afterthought" (Plato 428 BCE/1905, 225). The brothers were charged with giving the animals each good gifts and characteristics to ensure survival and prosperity. Epimetheus, living up to his name, distributed the gifts without first thinking about making sure that every animal received something (Plato,428 BCE/1905, 217). When it came time to give gifts to the human being, Epimetheus found that he had nothing left. Seeing that the human would be left in an intolerably perilous position, Prometheus intervened by stealing fire from heaven for human use (a crime for which he would pay dearly; Zeus would order that he be bound to a rock where an eagle would come to eat his ever-regenerating liver each day!). Leo Strauss (1953) once described the character of Epimetheus as he for whom "thought follows production" (117). Such a process did not have a good outcome for Epimetheus or for Prometheus, who ended up severely punished for the way he tried to clean up after his brother's mess. The story would make a good parable also for the production of the writing life. The Epimethean writer may have his or her moments – inspiration can elicit here and there some very powerful flourishes—but ultimately the failure to plan, the failure to think ahead and to prepare well for the activity of production, will have consequences just as disastrous for you as a writer as they were for Epimetheus. In what follows, we will be asking you to apply forethought (as well as the afterthought) of your reflection on your writing practice in order to ensure high production in your writing. Because we don't want your brother having to bail you out or finding himself chained to a rock, his liver for bird cuisine, and because we want you to succeed as a writer.

A Formula for Writing Productivity

What keeps writers from being productive? Many writers complain that they just can't find the time; others, that they don't have a good working environment in which to write; while still others feel that they lack focus in their writing sessions. Behind these three complaints can be found most of the major obstacles to writing productivity. What can we do to counteract these challenges?

Figure 6.1 is a representation of what we call a formula for writing productivity. While it is certainly not a magic formula, it does provide a way of organizing your writing and crafting good habits that will ensure that your hard work will pay off. There are four main ingredients to our formula. They work together and when well applied, they result in high levels of writing productivity. The four ingredients are the following: time, place and ritual, goals, and onus. We will consider each in turn.

Time

You can't write if you don't have time. It's as simple as that. But the simple matter of time can often become rather complicated. For example, you might have time available but not all time is equal. The

---

Careful forethought and planning about <u>Time + Place and Ritual</u>

+ Goals

+ Onus =

Writing Productivity

Figure 6.1. A Formula for Writing Productivity.

High productivity times	Low productivity times
• Drafting	• Searching databases
• Reading and outlining	• Downloading PDFs
• Thinking through the conceptualization of your project	• Footnotes
	• Bibliography

Figure 6.2. *Matching Time with Types of Work.*

kind of time you'll need to write will depend on the kind of writing that you're doing. So while having time is important, for many, writing tasks not just any time will do. The "deep work," as Cal Newport (2016) calls it, of the initial drafting and conceptualization of your project, for example, will in all likelihood require longer and more intense writing time-blocks than those dedicated to checking references and composing bibliography. What does this mean for you? It means that you will want to structure your writing times to account for the kind of work that you need to do, saving the more intensive work for when you are fresher and tackling the more menial tasks of bibliography and style checking for those low-energy times (see Figure 6.2).

Structuring your time in this way requires you to combine the best of the Promethean and Epimethean spirits. It requires that you reflect on yourself as a writer and researcher (afterthought) in order to plan your writing activity (forethought). When are you most fresh? What are the possibilities and constraints of your schedule? How can you negotiate these two sometimes competing answers to find the best possible times for your writing schedule? Being productive in your writing will necessitate examination of your habits, of your own personal biological clock, and of your personal and professional responsibilities outside of writing. Every writer is different. The nineteenth-century French novelist Balzac was for a time the earliest of risers, awaking at midnight to write furiously in marathon fashion through to the noon hour, with the aid of coffee consumed superabundantly (Lawton 1910, 75); the nineteenth century English novelist Trollope (1883/1912) would be at his writing desk at 5:30 in the morning and would do all of his writing before doing anything else, including dressing for the day and indulging in breakfast (236). The key is to find what works best for you.

The presupposition of this way of approaching writing time is that you are scheduling your day not according to tasks that need to be completed but according to time blocks (Newport 2016, 223-25). We'll talk more about goals below, but this approach entails thinking in advance (forethought) about what needs to be done and assigning a limited amount of time to each task. Rather than saying to yourself, "Today I will write the 'discussion' section of my paper," you think instead, "Today I have three hours of time to write. I need to write my discussion section. How long should that take? Probably two hours. I have an hour left over. I will probably be tired after drafting but I can start on the references page since that isn't too labor intensive." The advantage of this method, as can be seen from this example, is that you anticipate more what can be done in a given period of time and by giving yourself only the necessary time, you are likely to spend that time more efficiently. If a task takes more time, you can always revise your schedule accordingly on the fly: "Well, it took 2-1/2 hours to write the discussion. So I will spend the last half hour on my references, and we'll see how far I get." Implementing time blocks in this way instead of task lists will help you accomplish more with the same amount of time.

Place and Ritual

Even with the all the time in the world used as well as possible, no writer will be successful without a conducive writing environment. As with the matter of time, you will need to consider what space arrangements are most ideal for you. Some writers would thrive in Hugo Gernsback's Isolator (see Figure 6.3); others prefer not total sense deprivation but instead the ambient noise of the local Starbucks. We knew one writer who wrote her dissertation on a continuous daily migration from the bagel shop to the library to her home. She found that for her a new setting would provide a needed refresh throughout the writing day. Another dissertator wrote the bulk of his project at a sandwich shop chatting it up with the regulars in between writing sessions. He found the comradery and social atmosphere provided the perfect inspiration for composition. We can contrast this with another writer we knew who found it impossible to make progress in such settings precisely because the repeat customers would eventually try to strike up conversation after seeing him there frequently, which he found unbearably distracting. The ancient Greek maxim is know thyself. It's couldn't be truer in thinking about an ideal space for writing.

Knowing yourself may also mean taking into account your personal situation. Not everyone has large blocks of time. Not everyone has a quiet environment for writing. Many people have to navigate the difficult waters of research and writing while attending school full-time,

The author at work in his private study aided by the Isolator. Outside noises being eliminated. the worker can concentrate with ease upon the subject at hand.

Figure 6.3. *Hugo Gernsback's Isolator. Source: "The Isolator" Science and Invention, vol. 13, no. 3, July 1925.*

holding down a day job, raising a family, living in cramped quarters with roommates. If you have these greater challenges, don't lose heart. There are plenty of examples of great writers who did their best work amid difficult circumstances. Ernest Hemingway began his writing career penniless (Fleming 1996, 141). William Faulkner wrote the modernist masterpiece *As I Lay Dying* while working the night shift at the university power plant, using a wheelbarrow as a makeshift writing desk (Blotner 1974/2005, 248). Graham Greene scibbled *Brighton Rock* amid the cries of his newborn baby and in between other writing projects (Sherry 1990, 608). Paul Silvia (2007), author of *How to Write a Lot*, gives this testimony:

> Unproductive writers often bemoan the lack of 'their own space' to write. I'm not sympathetic to this creaky excuse. I've never had my own room as a home office or private writing space. In a strong of small apartments and houses, I wrote on a small table in the living room, in my bedroom, in the guest bedroom, in the master bedroom, and even (briefly) in a bathroom. I wrote this book [*How to Write a Lot*] in the guest bedroom in my house. Even now, after writing all those books and articles and after buying a house, I still don't have my own space at home to write. But I don't need it—there's always a free bathroom. (20-21).

Silvia brings up an important point that touches on mindset. You've got to have the "write" attitude. You will encounter obstacles and difficulties of every imaginable kind in your writing. What matters is how you deal with this adversity. There will be plenty of opportunity to make excuses and to find new ways to procrastinate. You can let that adversity be a stumbling block or, like Silvia, you can let nothing stop you from being productive.

Brian Chappell, one of Cal Newport's deep workers, tells us that he dons the same old flannel shirt every day for his break of dawn writing sessions (with a near identical backup on hand for laundry days). Peter Selgin (2003) has written of his writer friend who would wear different hats during different stages of the writing process: one hat for initial drafting ("a red baseball cap with KEROUAC stitched in gold over the visor") and another for editing ("Chinese, tutti-frutti, shaped like a funnel") (214). Ritual is important to productivity because it helps to forge and maintain habituated behavior, even in times of stress and difficulty. The power of ritual is ultimately the power to integrate the intellectual with the emotional, providing a strong force for the regulation of behavior, keeping you composed and able to perform at high levels (Ozenc and Hagan 2019, 5–6). Rituals also allow you to flip the switch into writing mode quickly and efficiently, helping you to go to that special mental "happy writing place" even (and especially) when you don't feel like banging away on the keyboard.

Goals

You can't get to your destination if you don't know where you are going. Having clearly defined goals is an essential part of being productive. Goals help you to focus and setting goals well will allow you to make the best use of your time.

Figure 6.4 is a graphic representing The Writing Loop, which is a simple but effective process to ensure fruitful goal setting. The green circle indicates your initial start point for the cycle of setting your goals, working toward meeting them, assessing, resetting, and beginning again. This procedure—carried out from day to day, week to week, month to month—will ensure that you stay on track in your writing. At the level of the individual session, it is best to assess and reset your goals at the end of the writing time-block. Why at the end? Because at that point, you have snorkeled down to the ocean floor of the depths of your project and are surrounded by all of the moss and minoes, the complexities and nuance, of your project. You are about to come up for air, finish your session, and go off to other things: family, school, work,

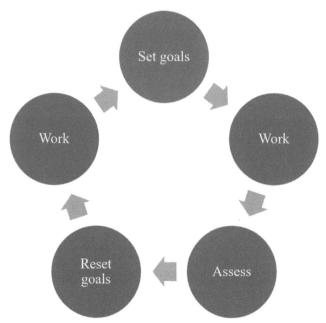

Figure 6.4. *The Writing Loop.*

recreation. By the time you return to your writing, a day or two, or more, may have passed. You are likely to have forgotten all about what was going at the ocean floor in your previous session. Having a list of goals and some notes from the deep dive will help you to express your way back down.

The Writing Loop, though, is a process that can and should be used beyond the individual session. You will need to set, work, assess, and reset also for your short-term, midterm, and long-term goals—which will be key for your semester-long projects and for the dissertation. For a semester-long project, for example, you'll want to check in on your progress each week to see if you are still on track and what adjustments might need to be made.

You should set goals and use The Writing Loop method to track your progress. But you also need to have the right mindset about what goals are for. Too often writers get discouraged and become preoccupied with goals. When they do this, goals become ends in themselves and become counter-productive. It may sound strange, but goals are paradoxically not ends in and of themselves. The goal is merely a means to the end of writing a lot. If the end becomes the focus, it can end up derailing your productivity. While you should be noticing patterns and making adjustments—for example, if you are consistently failing to meet your goals, you may need to readjust your expectations—it is important to remain focused on your progress and on how goals are facilitating your writing progress.

Onus

The prolific American author and librarian Lawrence Clark Powell once said that "Writing is a solitary occupation. Family, friends, and society are the natural enemies of the writer" (Kelner 2005, 49). Powell's view is widely held, but the truth is that a healthy writing process, the kind that produces writing of high quality, usually involves collaboration of various kinds. Rather than enemies, family and friends can often be a source of tremendous support to you in your writing. And editors, professors, and other readers will more than likely have significant, positive influence on the success of your projects. Most academic books—and many articles—include an "Acknowledgements" section. The purpose of that section is to recognize and thank all of the people who helped to make the book or article a reality. It often includes friends and family—Powell's supposed enemies—as well as colleagues and professional editors (Powell himself composed and included an "Acknowledgments" page in his books).

This kind of community and collaborative support in your writing can take many forms. One element of collaboration that is connected particularly to writing output has to do with what we call "onus": by which we mean those measures of accountability that you can create for your writing. You may be used to having deadlines and assignments preset for you by your teachers. As a graduate student, however, often the onus will be on you. We suggest that you share the onus by making the burden of deadlines and productivity a shared burden. Put it not all "on you" but find ways to have the burden fall "on us" as it were. How do you do that? And who can that "us" be?

There are many ways to help you build structures of community and of exterior accountability. One strategy is the writing group. You could collaborate with your classmates to form a group that meets every week on campus before or after classes. The work that these groups do can be varied, depending on member preference and need. The group can be more consultative or supportive in character. It can be an avenue for everyone to update each other on work in progress, which can be cathartic but also can help to foster accountability. Or, alternatively, a writing group can be more centered on getting writing done. At the Writing Center at The Catholic University of America, we hold each summer a Dissertation Boot Camp, a common type of event for many writing centers at institutions with doctoral programs. The Camp provides a productive environment and space for reflection through amenities and speakers, but one of the most powerful aspects of the week is the simple fact that all of these dissertators are put together in the same room and made to write together for two ninety-minute blocks in the morning and two in the afternoon. Participants have often remarked how much more productive they are in this setting and they attribute this productivity in part to the mere fact of being in the same room together with colleagues engaged in the same endeavor.

If writing groups are not possible for you, another strategy would be the "writing pact." A writing pact is a flexible way to create account-ability that doesn't take a lot of coordination beforehand. For example, if you know that you and a classmate are free on Saturday mornings, consider entering into a "writing pact" together. This can be as easy as emailing your colleague with a short note: "Let's pledge to work non-stop from 10a-2p drafting today." Or if you're having trouble hunkering down on the dissertation, consider emailing your spouse or significant other telling them that you are formally setting a deadline and you will have twenty new pages delivered to them by the end of the week (or maybe every week). Your university's writing center can also be a great source of accountability, in addition to a place where you can get help with your writing. Making regular appointments in advance with your writing center can be a great way to ensure that you're making progress on your longer projects by facilitating longer-term scheduling and mak-ing sure you keep to deadlines.

By enacting these strategies, you can help to make the onus a com-munity endeavor that is not simply "on you."

Know Thyself

To return that ancient Greek maxim, we will close the chapter by thinking about how the strategies and practices offered here may be put to best use by you. Knowing yourself can help you to know what strategies you need the most. As an epilogue to our formula, we want to introduce the work of Gretchen Rubin on the Four Tendencies. Rubin (2017) outlines different personality types and shows how these types react differently to inner and outer expectations.

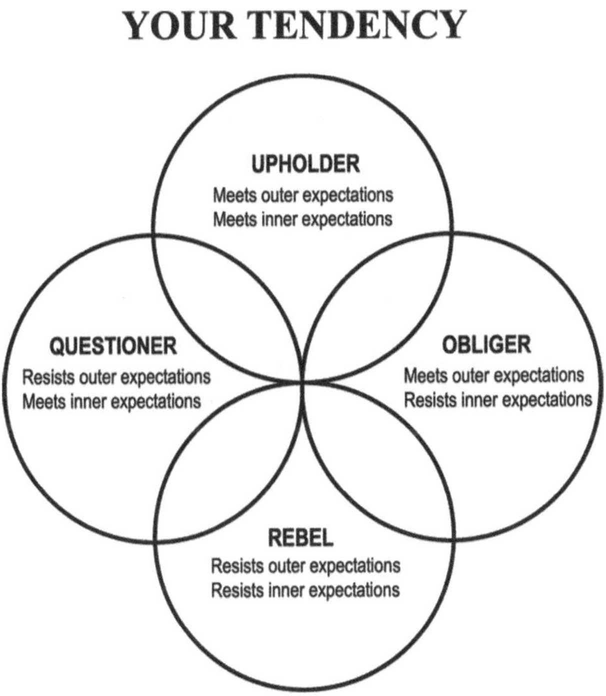

YOUR TENDENCY

UPHOLDER
Meets outer expectations
Meets inner expectations

QUESTIONER
Resists outer expectations
Meets inner expectations

OBLIGER
Meets outer expectations
Resists inner expectations

REBEL
Resists outer expectations
Resists inner expectations

Figure 6.5. *Rubin's Four Tendencies.*

Obligers meet outer expectations but have difficulty with inner expectations. If you're an obliger, sharing the burden of "onus" may be particularly important for you. Make every effort in this case to seek community and exterior accountability.

Questioners are in some ways the inverse of obligers in that they will meet inner expectations but have difficulty with outer expectations. Questioners have a strong drive to understand for themselves what they are being tasked to do. But because questioners can have trouble knowing when to move from questioning and analyzing to decisions and action, they may also need exterior accountability, if for other reasons than the obligers.

Upholders meet both inner and outer expectations. They struggle, however, when they don't have a clear sense of what is expected. For upholders, goal setting is extremely important. Upholders flourish when they have clear goals, but they also need to have a healthy approach to goals that includes flexibility and the willingness to make adjustments when needed.

Rebels are aptly named, for they shun both inner and outer expectations. They love a challenge but have difficulty following the rules and conventions of the group. If you're a Rebel, you probably won't be motivated by writing groups or other external forms of accountability. Rebels may find that they need to "own" their goals in order to be motivated to achieve them.

These categories can't capture your full complexity as a unique human individual, of course. But they can be useful lens for considering what motivates you and where your strengths and weaknesses lie related to productivity. It is important to understand your own motivations and ways of making sense of the work that you do as you give some forethought to building your optimal writing schedule and regimen.

Practice Exercises

Answer the following questions related to your productivity.

Productivity Analysis

1. Time
   a. What times of the day and days of the week do I have available to write on a regular basis?
   b. When do I usually do my best writing work during the day?
   c. When am I available but not at my best?
2. Place/Environment
   a. What spaces do I usually write best in?
      i. Do I prefer public or private spaces?
      ii. Do I prefer ambient noise or perfect silence?
   b. What rituals do I already have built into my writing routine? What rituals might I incorporate?
3. How might I incorporate accountability and community into my writing and researching process?
4. Which of Rubin's four personality types do I think I best conform to? How might I take advantage of my personality strengths and counteract my weaknesses in my writing and researching regimen?

References

Blotner, J. 2005. *Faulkner: A Biography*. Jackson: University Press of Mississippi. (Original work published in 1974.)

Brookshire, R. H. and S. B. Brundage. 2016. *Writing Scientific Research in Communication Sciences and Disorders*. San Diego: Plural Publishing.

Daiker, D. A. 1999. "Learning to Praise." In *Sourcebook for Responding to Student Writing*, edited by R. Straub, 153–163. Cresskill, NJ: Hampton Press. (Original work published in 1989.)

Daly, J., and M. Miller. 1975. "The Empirical Development of an Instrument to Measure Writing Apprehension." *Research in the Teaching of English* 9 (3), 242–249. http://www.jstor.org/stable/40170632.

Durant, Will. 1930. *The Story of Philosophy: The Lives and Opinions of the Greater Philosophers*. New York: Simon and Schuster.

Field, S. 1984. *The screenwriter's workbook*. New York: Dell Publishing.

Fleming, R. E. 1996. Hemingway's late fiction: Breaking new ground, 128-48. *The Cambridge Companion to Ernest Hemingway*. Edited by Scott Donaldson. Cambridge, UK: Cambridge University Press.

Hult, C.A. 2016. *The handy English grammar answer book*. Canton, MI: Visible Ink Press.

Kelner, Stephen P. 2005. *Motivate your writing!: Using motivational psychology to energize your writing life*. Hanover: University Press of New England.

Lawton, F. 1910. *Balzac*. London: Grant Richard Ltd.

Newport, Cal. 2016. *Deep work: Rules for focused success in a distracted world*. New York: Grand Central Publishing.

Ozenc, K. and M. Hagan. 2019. *Rituals for work: 50 ways to create engagement, shared purpose, and a culture that can adapt to change*. Hoboken, NJ: Wiley.

Pajares, F. 2003. "Self-efficacy beliefs, motivation, and achievement in writing: A review of the literature." *Reading & Writing Quarterly*, 19, 139–158.

Pajares, F., and M. J. Johnson. 1994. "Confidence and competence in writing: The role of self-efficacy, outcome expectancy, and apprehension." *Research in the Teaching of English* 28 (3), 313–331.

Plato. BC/1905. *The Myths of Plato*. Trans. J.A. Stewart. London: Macmillan and co.

Selgin, Peter. 2003. "Revision: Real writers revise." *Gotham Writers' Workshop: Writing fiction: The practical guide from New York's acclaimed creative writing school*. 213–36. Edited by Alexander Steele. New York: Bloomsbury.

Sherry, N. 1990. *The life of Graham Greene: 1904–1939*. New York: Penguin Books.

Silvia, Paul J. 2007. *How to write a lot: A practical guide to productive academic writing*. American Psychological Association.

Strauss, Leo. 1953. *Natural right and history*. Chicago: The University of Chicago Press.

Trollope, Anthony. 1912. *Autobiography of Anthony Trollope*. New York: Dodd, Mead and Company. Original works published in 1883.

CHAPTER 7

Organizing and Developing the Manuscript

The first sentence can't be written until the final sentence is written.
—Joyce Carol Oates, WD

Introduction

THE doctoral nursing student stares at a blank page. The assignment due date nears. Tension mounts. Most writers have experienced the pressure to develop a "story," and for nurses in a graduate program, the traditional story focus is science and its application to health and illness. Developing the story requires that the writer sufficiently master the topic of interest and that involves research, reading, critical evaluation, and synthesis to the proposed work—in this case a doctoral-level assignment.

The same process applies to the DNP graduate eager to disseminate innovative project results through publication. The process differs little and is easily transferable from the academic to the practice setting. In this chapter, we tackle the process of *organizing and developing* a manuscript to influence the reader without altering the evidence that underpins the topic under discussion.

Spinning or Finding the Angle for the "Story"

In developing a manuscript, the writer begins by acknowledging the intended audience (Moxley 2017; Crestodina 2013) and the purpose and genre of the paper (Rogers 2019). The importance of determining the makeup of the audience cannot be overstated. If C-Suite nurse leaders are the audience for a new clinical program business plan, the writer will focus the narrative in a fashion meant to engage nurses in top leadership positions. In this instance, attention may center on cost-benefit analyses, nurse workload impact, department reconfiguration, and/or clinical outcome improvement. However, if the audience is the clinical nurse practicing at the bedside, a warranted shift in focus may target program feasibility, the restructuring of care delivery at point-of-service, sufficient staff to support the proposed program, and/or engagement in in the new venture by other healthcare professionals. Regardless of the topic, the writer must identify the audience as well as the manuscript's intended purpose.

Developing the Thesis or Problem

Once the target audience is solidified, the writer must develop a thesis (Suazo 2017; Laue and Montgomery, n.d.). The thesis is the central argument of a paper that identifies the issue or problem that the writer wishes to address, and the "angle" from which the writer views the issue. The content of the document will focus on how the writer develops and defends the problem from the writer's angle or viewpoint (Rogers 2019; Reye 2017a).

To succeed, the writer must research the topic by exhausting seminal and contemporary published work to demonstrate the writer's subject matter expertise. Only then will the writer know if the thesis qualifies as a legitimate proposition based on evidence. When developing a thesis or problem statement for conducting research, although the writer/ researcher may yet to prove the thesis, the researcher must demonstrate immersion in the literature sufficient to build a solid case regarding the efficacy of the proposed research.

Writers find that one of the most difficult challenges is developing the thesis statement (Suazo 2017). Novice writers tend to write wandering paragraphs *around* a topic or problem and fail to clearly develop or convey their argument. One way in which writers can address this challenge is to compose one sentence—no more—that states clearly and succinctly the issue or problem the writer intends to address. However, many writers initially find this task very difficult. Consider the following two examples:

- "The Affordable Care Act (ACA) enacted in 2010 sought to provide increased access to health care and improve care coordination (*Is this the thesis?*) (Emmer 2013). The inclusion of care coordination addressed the disjointed nature of America's current health care delivery (*Is this the thesis?*) The care coordination of the ACA includes collaboration between all healthcare professionals in an attempt to provide patients with better outcomes (*Is this the thesis?*)."

and

- "Electronic Health Record (EHR) DHHS requirements place a significant burden on the nursing workforce (*Is this the thesis?*). The widespread adoption and "meaningful use" of EHRs is a national priority (*Is this the thesis?*). EHR use has the potential to reduce the overuse, underuse, and misuse of healthcare services with the use of decision support elements. The most effective way to meet the meaningful use criteria is through the adoption of decision support elements, but less than 2 percent of United States hospitals have EHR systems (*Is this the thesis?*) meeting these requirements (Kutney-Lee and Kelly 2011)."

In both examples, the reader struggles to determine exactly what the writer intends to argue in the coming narrative. The following examples illustrate the value of a clearly defined theses:

- "Nurses function in very stressful working environments that interfere with providing consistent quality care and result in 'missed nursing care' or the failure to deliver prescribe treatment." (Nicholson 2019).

and

- "Neonatal intensive care nursing lacks the tools necessary to provide optimum hemodynamic maintenance to mechanically ventilated premature infants secondary to a lack of real-time, continuous, and clinically relevant data." (Weaver 2018)

Again, writers should aim for one clearly written sentence appropriately "angled" with the writer's point-of-view and intent of the upcoming argument that the writer plans to development in the narrative.

Developing an Angle of Vision

Exactly what is an "angle of vision"? An angle of vision refers to how a writer manipulates a narrative to get a specific message to readers (Florida International University, n.d.). It references the author's point-of-view and enables the writer to control how the information the writer intends to impart will unfold. Effectively, the angle of vision gives "power" to the author, forcing the reader to journey a path created by the author (Rogers 2019; Stevens 2014). Because the writer works to manipulate the perspective of the reader, it is a powerful tool, and doing so elevates the importance of this technique for authors and readers alike.

To successfully develop an "angle," the writer must communicate intelligently based on the intended audience. For instance, one nurse might view the opportunity to publish a successful project in a peer-reviewed journal as a potential positive professional experience, whereas another may dread the process, noting the work required. An author describing one nurse versus the other nurse can craft a narrative that sways the reader's viewpoint to align with the angle of vision expressed by the author. For example:

- "In completing her Capstone Scholarly Paper, the masters student enjoyed writing and developed the assignment for publication because of her commitment to knowledge dissemination."

versus

- "Regardless of the Capstone Scholarly Paper describing an innovative project, the masters' student disliked the effort required in manuscript development and opted to disseminate knowledge by submitting her work for poster consideration at a national conference."

Each time a writer develops a document, the writer imbeds their angle of vision—their viewpoint. In these two examples the reader aligns with the notion that either the publication is worth the effort or developing a poster presentation is less work.

Framing the Manuscript

Creating the frame for an assignment or publication involves "organizing, perceiving, representing, interpreting, simplifying, and communicating about reality" (Johnson and Rulo 2019). Similar to "angle of vision," framing influences how a reader perceives written work. The author does not manipulate facts, but uses them to describe, generate discussion, or elicit reader reaction about complex issues. When framing an article or assignment, understanding the cause and effect of relationships and sequencing the presentation enables a writer to influence the reader. Using comparisons—differences or similarities and severity of each—can produce the same effect.

Begin framing the manuscript's central contribution and communicate it in the title (Mensh and Kording 2017). The title describes the intent of the manuscript, its primary topic, and its envisioned impact. In developing the title, opt for few words and focus on quality, remembering that readers determine their interest in reading the author's work primarily based on the title (Casanave and Li 2015). Remember that the title is a distillation of the entire manuscript. Returning to it periodically as the narrative develops serves to re-align the author with the intent of the work. Further, it assists the writer to remain on track and within the boundaries of the frame.

One area that writers largely overlook is the importance of *defining* the issue or problem clearly and concisely as previously discussed. It is part of developing the "frame". Breaking the issue into component parts and immersing in the evidentiary details ultimately enables the writer to develop a rich discussion that fully frames the issue. Without building the foundation based on evidence and all its details, the narrative falls short, lacking thorough analysis and synthesis to the topic of interest.

Another useful tool in the framing process is researching cogent timelines that may identify critical milestones or an evolutionary pro-

TABLE 7.1. Summary of Ten Rules and Indication of Rule Violation.

Rule	Violation Indication
1. Focus on one big idea.	Readers cannot give a one sentence summary.
2. Write for the reader-who-does-not-know.	Readers do not "get" the paper.
3. Use context, content, conclusion align with beginning, body, ending.	Readers ask why something matters or what it means.
4. Optimize logical flow.	Readers stumble on sections of the text
5. Abstract: Compact summary of the paper.	Readers cannot give the "elevator pitch" of the author's work after reading it.
6. Introduction: Why the paper matters.	Readers show little interest in the paper.
7. Justified conclusions.	Readers do not agree with author's conclusions.
8. Preempt criticism, give future impact.	Readers left with unanswered criticisms and/or questions.
9. Allocate time wisely.	Readers struggle to understand the author's central contribution despite effort.
10. Reiterate the story.	Paper rejected by editors or reviewers.

Mensh, B., & Kording, K. (2017). Ten simple rules for structuring papers. *PLoS computational biology, 13*(9), e1005619. doi:10.1371/journal.pcbi.1005619

cess related to the topic under discussion (Mensh and Kording 2017). Whether it is the massive increase in the number of DNP programs and students resulting from the Institute of Medicine Report in 2010 or the showstopping lack of nursing faculty desperately needed in academic programs, researching data and framing the topic based on factual evidence strengthens the quality and rigor of manuscript content. One of the key reasons for this is that a successful frame assists the reader-who-does-not-know to link the writer's perspective to their current understanding of the topic, while also exposing them to different perspectives or viewpoints (Johnson and Rulo 2019).

Ten Rules for Narrative Framing

Mensh and Kording (2017, 9) suggest ten rules that should guide manuscript development, especially in the sciences. Table 7.1 lists the rules and offers how one can measure if the writer violated any rule on the list.

Structuring or Organizing the Manuscript

One of the most important parts of writing is creating an outline of the content that the writer intends to cover. Manuscripts generally have a three part structure, referred to as the "narrative arc": a beginning, a well-developed body or middle, and an end. The narrative arc illustrated in Figure 7.1 underscores the role of the three components in

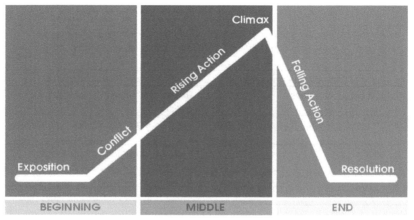

Figure 7.1. The Narrative Arc. Courtesy of: Joyce E. Johnson.

manuscript development. Note the beginning sets the tone and foundation and hooks the reader by presenting a cogent an enticing argument. The middle offers substantial evidence, critical analysis, and synthesis, enabling the writer to "prove" the argument or their point-of-view. The end or conclusion effectively summarizes cogent points contained throughout the manuscript.

In addition, the three components contain structural elements: context, content, and conclusion (Mensh and Kording, 2017). The context must alert the reader to what gap the narrative will fill and sets the author's work apart from previous publications. The context answers the "So What?" question. It conveys why the author's work is important and worthy of reading.

The content is the work the author wishes to convey to support the theses and address the identified problem. It is the argument that advances the author's viewpoint, enriches the argument, and sways the reader to align with the author's perspective. The conclusion interprets the evidence presented, sequentially summarizing its impact and justifying the original theses.

These three components—context, content, and conclusion—overlay the three part manuscript structure: the beginning, the body, and the end, with the beginning setting the stage, offering evidence, and building a solid foundation (Jericho Writers 2019). The title and introduction "hook" the reader and set the stage and foundation. The body logically defines and frames the topic based on evidence; it is written *for the reader who does not know, not for the writer who does*. The conclusion verifies what the reader understood the writer intended to convey.

Developing the Manuscript

Although the structure of the narrative drives the general structure of the entire manuscript, the writer journeys through a series of steps before achieving a well-developed article or graduate level assignment. One of the most important steps is the development of a good outline for the paper (Reye 2017b). The outline should offer detail and depth, noting all headings, sections, and subsections that the author envisions necessary to cover the argument and sway the reader toward the author's perspective. A well-developed outline serves to guide the writer, keep the narrative on track with the topic, and retain audience interest. It assists in organizing multiple ideas about a topic and can be key in keeping the writer focused (University of Southern California 2019).

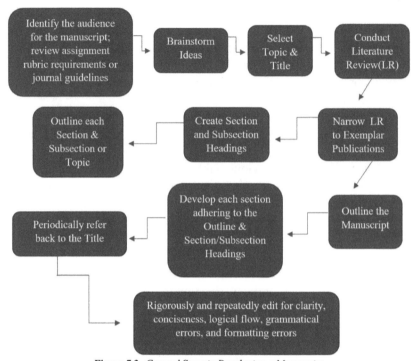

Figure 7.2. *General Steps in Developing a Manuscript.*

Finally, a strong outline notes each main topic and related subtopics and helps the writer to focus on the strength of the argument and the rigor of its logic.

Figure 7.2 illustrates the general steps in developing an academic paper or a paper intended for publication. Note the important aspects of identifying the audience and topic, conducting a thorough literature review to render exemplars, creating a detailed outline, referring back to the title, and editing, editing, editing.

Writing Abstracts

Abstracts contain the same components and structure as the body of a narrative. The difference is in the finite distillation of information condensed into its most concise form found in an abstract (Morgan 2019). In developing an abstract, the writer should first understand any requirements for writing the abstract. Journal publications, coursework submissions, or work projects offer guidelines or rubrics, such as maximum length and/or style requirements. The abstract essentially provides a review of each section of the manuscript, and the writer should aim for one sentence to capture the cogent section point. Although the beginning of the abstract will inform the reader of the topic, gap, and intent, the content will be addressed by explaining important and logical components of the topic that the author addressed in the manuscript (Morgan 2019). Finally, the conclusion offers the author the opportunity to summarize the rich information nuggets that flow from the evidence-based narrative (George Mason University 2019).

Steps in writing an abstract include the following (Morgan 2019):

1. Identifying the purpose and the import of the topic.
2. Explaining the issue or problem—offering evidence.
3. Explaining the critical analyses and syntheses of the evidence.
4. Describing or offering findings—the "so what."
5. Closing by addressing the meanings of the findings and the future impact.

Remember, at every point along the way from section to sub-section, the writer must reorient the reader to the thesis's topic. Further, in developing the rich content, the writer should periodically return to the central idea as abstract development progresses. If the writer errs and "zig-zags" to multiple topics, the result will serve to confuse the reader, interrupt logical flow, and get the writer off-course, netting a torturous document (George Mason University 2019).

A Word about Beginnings and Endings

Beginnings

Not surprisingly, good beginnings give the reader the sense that they are on a journey, one that they grow to anticipate. The beginning must hook the reader or the reader will fail to engage and read on. Developing an interesting "angle," even for an academic paper, sets the writer apart and elevates reader interest. Consider the following example of an introduction that invites and hooks the reader:

- "The patients definitely sense that we're a lot more stressed now. We're spending three hours more per day—and that's no exaggeration—just trying to get caught up."

These are the words of an American physician who is struggling to practice medicine in the shifting landscape of medical practice today. There is no doubt that medical practice has been irrevocably altered by the introduction of and adaptation to electronic medical records (EMRs) and the regulations associated with the passage of the Affordable Care Act (ACA) in 2010. This article presents an overview of EMRs in medical practice, a summary of the ACA's impact on medical practice, physician perspectives on the new practice landscape and their retirement readiness, and the results of a new national physician survey that offer insights into today's practice environment and medical practice in the future." (Morrissey and Johnson 2017).

Although good beginnings set the pace for the entire manuscript (Johnson and Rulo 2019), it is surprising that the best beginnings are written last. Johnson and Rulo (2019) suggest that the creative writing process includes a significant portion of discovery that assists the writer to refine their viewpoint, fine-tune arguments, and arrive at conclusions logically. Therefore, this counter-intuitive recommendation helps ensure that the beginning "matches" the rest of the manuscript that flows from a serious literature review, critical analyses, and syntheses.

Endings

After the writer has invested considerable sweat equity in developing a quality narrative, sometimes the writer loses steam in crafting the ending. Racing through this important part of a manuscript can turn a great narrative on its edge. This is because the ending answers two very important questions: "So what?" and "Now what?". With a preponderance of evidence justifying the writer's argument, passing up the opportunity to link the writer's viewpoint with the future intent of the reader nets the author very little. The following example illustrates an effective ending:

"Whether changes in the new health legislation are large and sweeping or small and incremental remains to be seen. What is clear from this new national survey of American's physicians is that the landscape of contemporary medical practice has become a high-tech, highly regulated, stressful work environment which will continue to change in the years to come. The impact of this changing landscape on physician preparation for retirement suggests that significant challenges await physicians who have yet to develop a solid retirement planning strategy. In the absence of such a strategy, many are faced with limited early retirement options and a diminished lifestyle when they reach retirement age. Significant health-care industry pressures, rapidly changing technological requirements and long-standing physician commitment to preserving safe patient care, challenge the medical profession and contribute to a rapid and potentially troublesome future." (Morrissey and Johnson 2017).

The writer's primary job in closing the manuscript is to link the content of the manuscript to the reader by envisioning a future course of action, generating ideas, or enriching the reader's knowledge of the topic (Johnson and Rulo 2019). It is the ending that provides the author with one final opportunity to impress the reader and persuade the reader to appreciate the topic from the writer's point of view.

This chapter focused on framing a manuscript and discussed the components of the narrative arc: beginning, middle, and ending. The importance of finding an angle for a "story" set the stage for clarity in thesis development and the need for underpinning evidence. Narrative framing rules provided structure to organizing the manuscript and practice exercises are intended to refresh learned knowledge.

Practice Exercises

Part A: Developing the Theses or Problem

The following narrative contains an unclear thesis or problem statement. Write the thesis or problem statement in a concise and coherent sentence.

> The U.S. population is expected to increase by eighteen percent, to 349 million, between 2005 and 2025. (reference). The small numbers of physicians that choose primary care as a career has decreased in recent years, with this decrease and the large increase in the aging population we suffer from a compounding problem. With this growth we will experience massive demographic shifts stressing the primary care provider shortage.

Part B: Developing an Angle of Vision

Review the two narratives below, then answer the questions.

Narrative 1:

> I love coming to work each day at the Cancer Center. With the new treatment options for patients diagnosed with the disease, I see the promise of hope for each one. The lobby is brightly lit, flowers and greenery create a lovely atmosphere, and the healthcare personnel smile and emit positive, welcoming attitudes. Today, a cure might be found! I so enjoy helping my patients and working with my colleagues as we strive to made a positive difference for our patients.

Narrative 2:

> What a dreadful morning. Recent test results from of my patients have shown

that their cancers have metastasized further and I must discuss the results with them today. How I dread those upcoming meetings. No one wants to join me at these meetings. My colleagues keep themselves very busy so they can easily avoid me. I have no hope to offer these patients or their families.

Questions:

1. What are the differences in the environment described by the writers of these narratives?
2. What envisioned outcome differences have each writer expressed?
3. What personal viewpoints do these writers offer?
4. To which author are you most drawn? Why?

Part C: Framing the Narrative

1. Access any article in a peer-reviewed nursing journal. Read the *Introduction* ONLY. Identify three ways in which the author framed the narrative. Write a 250-word description of the techniques the author used in creating their "frame".
2. Review a previously submitted major assignment of 2,000 words or more written for a masters or doctoral program course. Write an abstract.

Part D: Developing the Manuscript

1. In 250 words or less, what are the three most important steps in the manuscript development process? Justify your selection.
2. In 250 words or less, in your opinion, what are the five most important roles for narrative framing. Justify your selection.

Part E: Beginnings and Endings

1. Read the beginning and ending of an article published in a peer-reviewed nursing journal. In 250 words or less, what can you derive from reading these two sections about the article?

References

Adair, L. 2010. "Find An Angle to Bring Your Subject to Life." *Writers Digest*. https://www.writersdigest.com/writing-articles/by-writing-goal/improve-my-writing/find-an-angle-to-bring-your-subject-to-life.

Casanave, C. P., and Y. Li. 2015. "Novices' Struggles With Conceptual and Theoretical Framing in Writing Dissertations and Papers for Publication." MDPI Academic Open Access Publishing. https://www.researchgate.net/publication/276158699_Novices'_Struggles_with_Conceptual_and_Theoretical_Framing_in_Writing_Dissertations_and_Papers_for_Publication.

Crestodina, A. 2013. "How to spin content without getting sick." Retrieved from https://www.orbitmedia.com/blog/content-spinning-how-to-spin-content/

Faith, J. 2011. "How to find an angle for your new article or post." Retrieved from http://joannefaith.com/2011/02/08/how-to-find-an-angle-for-an-article/

Florida International University n.d. "Angle of vision." Rhetoric and Writing at the College Level. Retrieved from https://writingpanther.wordpress.com/angle-of-vision/

George Mason University 2019. "Writing an Abstract." The Writing Center. Retrieved from https://writingcenter.gmu.edu/guides/writing-an-abstract

Hall, S. H. 2018. "Great marketers know these 4 techniques they teach in journalism school." The Daily Egg. Retrieved from https://www.crazyegg.com/blog/writing-techniques-journalists/

Indiana University Bloomington. "Writing abstracts." Writing Tutorial Services. Retrieved from https://wts.indiana.edu/writing-guides/writing-abstracts.html

Jericho Writers. 2019. Jericho Writers Club. "How to write beginnings, middles and ends." Retrieved from https://jerichowriters.com/story-structure-beginnings-middles-ends/

Johnson, J. E, and K. Rulo. 2019. "Problems in the Profession: How and Why Writing Skills Must Be Improved." *Journal of Professional Nursing* 35 (1), 57–64.

King, A. 2008. "How to find the angle." SUNY NCC Group. Retrieved from https://collegejournalism.wordpress.com/tag/how-to-find-the-angle/

Kowalski, W. 2014. "How to write beginnings, middles and endings. Writing for first time novelists." Createspace Independent Publishing Platform. Retrieved from https://jerichowriters.com/story-structure-beginnings-middles-endings

Laue, S., Montgomery, B. n.d. "Story angles and lead paragraph construction." Columbia Links: Columbia College Chicago. Retrieved from https://www.schooljournalism.org/wp-content/uploads/2013/09/Story-Angles-and-Lead-Paragraph-Construction-by-Sue-Laue-and-Billy-Montgomery.pdf

Mensh, B., and Kording, K. 2017. "Ten simple rules for structuring papers." *PLoS computational biology, 13*(9), e1005619. doi:10.1371/journal.pcbi.1005619

Morgan, M. 2019. "How to write an abstract." wikiHow. Retrieved from https://www.wikihow.com/Write-an-Abstract

Morrissey, S. P. and J. E. Johnson. 2017. "The Shifting Landscape: How Technology and Regulations Have Changed Physician Practice and Retirement." *Medical Research Archives* 5 (8), 1–14.

Moxley, J. 2017. "Consider your audience." Retrieved from https://writingcommons.org/consider-your-audience

Nicholson, K. 2019. "Exploring Relationships between Mindfulness, Job Stress, and Missing Nursing Care." (Unpublished doctoral dissertation proposal). The Catholic University of America, Washington, D.C. USA.

Reye, V. 2017a. "How to write an effective journal article and get it published." Inside Higher Ed. Retrieved from https://www.insidehighered.com/print/advice/2017/05/09/how-write-effective-journal-article-and-get-it-published-essay

Reye, V. 2017b. "Demystifying the journal article." Inside Higher Ed. Retrieved from https://www.insidehighered.com/advice/2017/05/09/how-write-effective-journal-article-and-get-it-published-essay

Rogers, T. 2019. "What is a story angle?" ThoughtCo Lifelong Learning. Retrieved from https://www.thoughtco.com/what-is-a-story-angle-2073756

Stevens, K. 2014. Writing 201: "What's your angle?" The Daily Post. Retrieved from https://dailypost.wordpress.com/author/kristastevens/

Suazo, M. 2017. "Choosing a thesis statement for your essay." Rhetoric and Writing at the College Level. Retrieved from https://writingpanther.wordpress.com/author/monicasuazo/

University of Richmond Writing Center Writer's Web. n.d. "Writing in the Disciplines: Journalism." Retrieved from http://writing2.richmond.edu/writing/wweb/journalism/begin.html

University of Southern California. 2019. "Making an outline—Organizing your social sciences research paper." Research Guides. Retrieved from https://libguides.usc.edu/writingguide/outline

Weaver, B. 2018. "Electrical Cardiometry during Mechanical Ventilation: A Correlational Study." (Unpublished doctoral dissertation proposal). The Catholic University of America, Washington, D.C. USA.

CHAPTER 8

The Tools and Rules of Writing

There is no artifice as good and desirable as simplicity.
—St. Frances de Sales

Introduction

STUDENTS in our writing and graduate course classes typically sigh and roll their eyes when the class agenda turns to the prerequisite rules of writing. Nevertheless, all students, aspiring writers, nurse authors, and even writers with a great deal of experience must know and follow the classic rules that govern English. This is especially critical for nurse authors who realize the importance of publishing scholarly work in professional nursing journals. Feedback from journal editors (Kennedy 2014) suggests that failure to follow the rules of writing significantly diminishes the likelihood of an article's acceptance in a professional journal.

In this chapter, we review the most important rules and tools of writing. For each, we have included an explanation, some examples, and a practice exercise. We have also described one of the tried-and-true techniques (scrubbing) that will help you polish your work. Since this chapter serves as a handy reference, we suggest that you copy the chapter and keep it near your computer for easy reference.

Active vs. Passive Voice

One of the most common writing challenges for nurses and all writers is learning how to write in the active voice. According to the University of Wisconsin-Madison Writing Center (2019), sentences written with passive voice "use more words, can be vague, and can lead to a tangle of prepositional phrases" (1). In contrast, using active voice can clarify and strengthen your writing by emphasizing the subject, or the source of the action, rather than the object of the action (Williams and Bizup 2014). The *Publication Manual of the American Psychological Association* (6th Edition, Section 3.18) recommends that writers use the active voice for clarity (APA 2010, 77). Most importantly for nurse authors, APA style is the preferred style for publications in the social sciences and in all scholarly works in nursing.

The voice of a verb tells us whether the subject of the sentence either *performs* the action or *receives the action* and *is acted upon*. In the *active voice*, the subject performs the action. For example: The scientist (*subject*) analyzed (*action verb*) the report (*object, receives the action*). In this sentence, the scientist is the subject who acts (by analyzing) the report, which is the object of the action.

In the passive voice, the subject does not perform the action. For example: the report (*subject*) was analyzed (*action verb*) by the scientist. (While the scientist in this sentence performs the action, as it does in its active version above, the scientist in this case is grammatically an object). Passive verbs consist of the verb "be" and the past participle of the main verb: *were analyzed, are worn, and was considered*. Other helping or auxiliary words may be present such as *have been analyzed, have been worn, and would have been considered*. There are some occasions when the passive voice may be acceptable, even necessary:

- Situations in which you want to highlight the action and not the actor: The new business proposal *was reviewed and approved* by the hospital's board of directors, top executives, and department managers. In this example, the most important idea is the review and approval of the proposal.
- A description of a situation in which the actor is unknown or not important: Each year, millions of young adults *are diagnosed* with opioid addictions. Here the emphasis is on the magnitude of the opioid crisis, and not the health care providers who make the diagnosis.
- A situation in which you wish to avoid or cannot name the actor: Post-operative instructions are often *misunderstood*. The focus of this statement is on a problem with patient instructions and not the patients who often misunderstand directions.
- An instruction: Smoking *is not allowed* in hospitals. In this case, the rule matters, and not the decision makers who created the rule.

(Strunk and White 2009, 18; University of Wisconsin Writing Center 2019, 1)

Although active voice is preferred in the introduction and discussion sections of nursing dissertations, the evidenced-based practice (EBP) scholarly project paper, masters theses and publications, there is one exception. Nurse researchers who struggle with writing about research methodology in the active voice will be relieved to learn that some use of the passive voice is acceptable in the methodology section of a dissertation, the EBP project paper or research publication (APA 2010; Cerejo 2013). This is acceptable because the purpose of the methods section is to describe the steps taken (such as recruiting subjects, conducting interviews, or collecting blood samples) vs. describing the doer, which in most cases will be the researcher.

Here is an example that illustrates an acceptable use of the passive voice when describing research methods:

Acceptable Passive Voice

NVivo software was used for qualitative data analysis.

Less Acceptable Active Voice

We used NVivo software to conduct qualitative data analysis. This is not desirable because pronouns should be avoided in most scholarly writing.

Less Acceptable Active Voice

The researcher used NVivo software to conduct qualitative data analysis. While acceptable, use of the term "researcher" is somewhat awkward and likely to challenge the scholarly writer.

Parallel Construction

Parallel construction is a writing technique in which a writer uses the same pattern or type of words in a sentence to show that all the ideas have the same importance. Parallel construction helps to guarantee consistency and clarity in writing, and to make writing more easily understood (Creigton 2013). According to Lumen Learning (2018), "Lack of parallel structure can disrupt the rhythm of a sentence, leaving it grammatically unbalanced. Proper parallel structure helps to establish balance and flow, enhancing readability and clarity," (1).

In general, parallel ideas are best expressed in parallel form, which means that nouns should be parallel with nouns, adjectives with adjectives, prepositional phrases with prepositional phrases, infinitives with infinitives, dependent clauses with dependent clauses, and so on. An example that is parallel: In any given day, a clinical nurse *dispenses* medications, *teaches* nursing students, and *conducts* an inventory of sterile supplies. An example that is not parallel: on any given day, a clinical nurse *dispenses* medications, *teaches* nursing students, and *is part* of a team that conducts an inventory of sterile supplies.

There are numerous ways to use parallel forms in writing (Luo 2019):

Items in a Series

A series includes three or more elements. Repetition of the construction is essential, but the tag word (such as "it" or "for") is not always required and may be omitted. This decision is a matter of preference and style.

- The nurse maintained a very busy schedule by *working* fifty hours per week in the hospital, *co-authoring* an article for a nursing journal, and *teaching* part-time at the local community college.
- The organization had a reputation *for its progressive policies, for its employee benefits*, and *for its public relations program*. Or to tighten your writing. . . . The organization is known for its *progressive policies, employee benefits*, and *public relations program*.

Coordinate Ideas

Coordinate ideas are connected by coordinating conjunctions such as *for, and, nor, but, or, yet*. This also includes comparisons created by *than* or *as*.

- Doctoral students often struggle to narrow their research topic *and* to write a systematic review of the literature.
- Working as a nurse practitioner is rewarding *but* demanding as well.

Vertical List that Follows a Colon

In any list—whether in a research proposal, print publication, or a PowerPoint presentation—*do not mix word forms* such as sentences, single words, verbs, gerunds, or different types of phrases that follow a colon:

- The order of business for the hospital executive meeting will be:
    —*reviewing* the subcommittee reports
    —*creating* a new process for billing
    —*revisiting* the need for a new recruitment campaign
- The first steps for inserting a Foley catheter include:
    —*Gather* equipment.
    —*Explain* procedure to the patient
    —*Assist* patient into supine position with legs spread and feet together
    —*Open* catheterization kit and catheter
    —*Prepare* sterile field
    —*Check* balloon for patency
    —*Coat* the distal portion (2–5 cm) of the catheter with lubricant
    —*Apply* sterile drape

Two-part Connectives

These include *either/or, neither/nor, not/only/but also*, and *both/and*. The construction following the first connective must match the second.

- *Either* the manager will edit the newsletter *or* he will hire a freelance editor.
- *Neither* the nursing supervisor *nor* the nurse manager could explain the recent increase in patient falls.

Restrictive vs. Non-restrictive Clauses

Novice writers often struggle with figuring out whether to use *that* or *which* in a sentence. Here are some easy-to-remember guidelines for these two terms that are sometimes called the "gatekeepers" of restrictive and non-restrictive clauses.

Use *that* to introduce clauses that are *restrictive*, or *essential*. An essential clause contains information that is *necessary* to understand the main idea of the sentence, and which limits the noun it modifies. Restrictive clauses are usually introduced by relative pronouns such as *that, who, whom*, or *whose*, and cannot be removed from a sentence without changing the sentence's meaning (Trafiss 2019). With a restrictive clause, you can often remove the relative pronoun entirely. Commas *do not* precede or follow restrictive clauses.

Here are some examples of sentence with restrictive clauses:

- The sales meeting that was held in Washington, DC was not well attended. Without the restrictive clause (that was held in Washington, DC), the reader would not understand which sales meeting was the subject of the sentence.
- A graduate nurse who has successfully completed a doctoral program and defended her/his doctoral dissertation or her EBP Scholarly Project Paper can be called doctor. Without the essential clause (who has successfully completed a doctoral program and defended her/his doctoral dissertation or her/his EBP Project Scholarly Paper), the remainder of the sentence does not make sense.

Use *which* to introduce clauses that *are non-restrictive* or *non-essential*. These clauses contain optional information that adds to the content but is *not necessary* to understand the main idea of the sentence. Commas are used to set off or surround non-restrictive clauses. An easy way to remember this is that non-essential clauses can be removed easily from a sentence, and that commas bracket or mark the removable part of the sentence (Trafiss 2019).

Here are some examples of sentences with non-restrictive clauses:

- The original budget, which was modified in 1999, has been completely changed by the new administration. The non-restrictive clause, *which was modified in 1999*, is not essential to the main idea of the sentence.
- Jane, who graduated from nursing school more than ten years ago, will soon begin a doctoral program at ABC University in Washington, DC. The non-restrictive clause, *who graduated from nursing school more than ten years ago*, is not essential to the main idea of the sentence.

A writer uses these types of clauses to help the reader distinguish between *necessary* and *nice-to-know, but unnecessary* information. One easy way to remember the difference between that and which is "*that* defines, *which* describes."

Subject-Verb Agreement

Subject-verb agreement should be simple, but it is often a problem in writing because there are specific rules to follow. It certainly is easier when there is just one subject in a sentence. Here are the rules that govern subject-verb agreement:

Rule #1: When there are two or more subjects joined by *and*, you must use a plural verb:

- The writer (*first subject*) *and* the editor (*second subject*) need (*plural verb*) a style manual.

Rule #2: If two or more subjects are preceded by *each* or *every*, you must use a singular verb:

- Each (*singular subject*) writer and editor needs (*singular verb*) a style manual.

Rule #3: When two or more subjects are joined by the connectives *either/or, neither/nor, nor*, or *or*, the verb must agree with the subject that is closest to the verb:

- *Either* a new printer *or* a new printer (*singular subject closest to verb*) is (*singular verb*) needed.
- *Neither* my staff members *nor* the writing consultant (*singular subject closest to verb*) is (*singular verb*) coordinating the arrangements of the training program.

Just a reminder that the following words are considered singular and require singular verbs: anybody, anyone, each, either, everybody, everyone, everything, neither, nobody, no one, nothing, one, somebody, someone, and something.

Exceptions

Some words are exceptions to the rules: *some, most, all, which, that,* and *who*. If the reference word (antecedent) is functioning as a single unit, the pronoun is singular. If the antecedent is functioning as multiple entities, the pronoun is plural (Purdue 2019).

- *Most evaluations were reviewed* by the manager, but *all* of the forms *have been submitted* on time.

Collective nouns usually take a singular verb because they are generally (but not always) considered a unit: audience, class, committee, community, company, crowd, department, division, faculty, family, group, jury, staff, and team. The exceptions are media and data.

- The review committee (*a unit*) has (*singular verb*) issued its reports. In this example, the committee has functioned as a unit.
- The members (*plural*) of the committee have (*plural verb*) issued a report. With this example, members is plural which requires a plural verb.
- The faculty (*a collective noun*) is (*a singular verb*) unhappy with the new tenure guidelines. In this example, the faculty is considered a group of faculty members.
- The media (*the plural of medium*) have (*plural verb*) been accused of having a left-leaning bias.
- The data (*plural of datum*) suggest (*plural verb*) that there has been a positive effect from the intervention.

Pronoun—Antecedent Agreement

This rule is similar to the one that governs subject-verb agreement. An antecedent (also known as a referent) is the word a pronoun refers to. A pronoun must agree in number (singular or plural), person (first, second or third), and if necessary, gender (feminine or masculine) with its antecedent.

Consider this example:

- David went to the personnel office, where he (*refers to David*) completed the forms for a leave of absence.

When the antecedents of a pronouns are joined by *either/or* or *neither/nor*, the pronouns must agree with the nearer antecedent.

- *Neither* the manager *nor* the administrative assistants (*nearer antecedent which is plural*) have completed their (*plural pronoun*) performance evaluation.
- *Neither* administrative assistants *nor* the manager (*nearer antecedent which is singular*) has completed his (*singular pronoun*) performance evaluation.

Use a singular pronoun when the antecedent is a singular indefinite pronoun such as anyone, everybody, anything, each, each one, everyone, someone, somebody, something, either, neither, no one, nobody, nothing, one, and another.

- Every (*singular indefinite pronoun*) company has its (*singular pronoun*) own vacation policy.
- Neither (*singular indefinite pronoun*) one of the approaches worked as well as it (*singular pronoun*) was expected to perform.

Whenever possible, avoid the use of gender-linked stereotypical pronouns such as he/she or he or she constructions.

- A consultant offers expert advice to his clients. An improved version of this sentence might read: Consultants offer expert advice to clients.

Who vs. Whom

When to use the pronouns *who* and *whom* can be confusing. The easiest way to determine which one to use is to clarify how the pronoun is functioning in the clause it introduces. Use *who* when the pronoun functions as a *subject*, and *whom* when the pronoun functions as an *object*.

One easy way to remember this is to use this easy trick. According to Allen (2019), "If you can replace the word with 'he' or 'she,' use *who*. If you can replace it with 'him' or 'her,' use *whom* (1). Substitute *who* for *he* and *him* for *whom*; then check to see if the sentence makes sense.

- *Who/Whom wrote the letter?*

   He wrote the letter. Therefore, *who* is correct.

- *Who/Whom should I vote for?*

   Should I vote for her? Therefore, *whom* is correct.

- *We all know who/whom pulled that prank.*

   This sentence contains two clauses: *we all know* and *who/whom pulled that prank*. We are interested in the second clause because it contains the *who/whom* choice. *He* pulled that prank. Therefore, *who* is correct.

- *We wondered who/whom the book was about.*

   This sentence contains two clauses: *we wondered* and *who/whom the book was about*. Again, we are interested in the second clause because it contains the *who/whom*. The book was about *her*. Therefore, *whom* is correct.

Modifiers

In English, the correct placement of modifiers is important to clarify the meaning intended by the writer. A modifier is a word that describes another word or phrase—an *adverb* (that describes an adjective, a verb, or another adverb), an *adjective* (that describes a noun or pronoun), or an entire phrase. Incorrect placement of a modifier can create an ambiguous or nonsensical meaning. Here are four types of modifiers (Lumen Learning 2019; Nichol 2012), with some examples that demonstrate the confusion and provide a helpful correction:

- *Squinting* (two way) modifiers—These modifiers are so confusing because the modifier is near two parts of a sentence and it is not clear to the reader if the modifier belongs to one part of the sentence or the other.
    —The manager told us *eventually* that the president would meet with us. Does this mean that the manager will tell us eventually or that the president would meet us eventually? The manager *eventually* told us that the president would meet with us. With this small correction, we now know that eventually relates to the manager and not the president.
- *Misplaced* modifiers—In this example, a modifier in the wrong place changes the meaning of the sentence, which now is quite funny.
    —For the holidays, the administrative staff decorated the office with the managers. Written this way, the staff used the managers as decorations! But consider this re-write: Along with the managers, the administrative staff decorated the office. With this change, we say that both the managers and the administrative staff decorated the office.
- *Dangling* modifiers—A modifier that in which a phrase does not modify the closest noun or pronoun and is too far away from the word it describes.
    —*Strolling through the park*, the squirrels scampered across our feet. In this example, the dangling modifier (*strolling through the park*) tells the reader that it is the squirrels are enjoying a nice stroll in the park! As we *strolled through the park*, the squirrels scampered across our feet. With this correction, the sentence has been clarified so that the speaker and his companion are strolling, and not the squirrels.
- *Disruptive* modifiers—A modifier that disrupts the flow of a sentence

because of its placement between the verb and the object. Consider this sentence: The nurse was instructed to *administer* every two hours the *dosage*. The problem is that *administer* and the *dosage* are not adjacent. Here is the new, improved sentence: The nurse was instructed to *administer* the *dosage* every two hours.

Transitions

For we writers, transitions are important tools that connect the various pieces of an article, and that help ensure a smooth flow to our writing. In our experience coaching nurse authors, choosing appropriate transitions is often challenging, and without appropriate transitions, writing can seem abrupt, choppy, or lacking "flow."

Contrary to what some believe, transitions are not merely words that embellish your writing and make it sound better. Transitions are the important connectors that smooth out the movement between sentences, paragraphs, and sections of an article. Transitions also serve as important signals to your readers, signals that alert them to an especially important idea or to a shift in topic. These signals help your readers understand the logic you used when writing your article. In many ways, transitions are the glue that binds your argument and logic together into a unified, coherent whole.

When deciding on transitions, the University of North Carolina Writing Center (2019) suggests that a writer must make several decisions:

- *How much of a transition is needed*? Sometimes in a longer work, you may transition to a new topic by summarizing the previous topic and then suggesting that you are moving on to the next. However, in shorter pieces that you have organized very logically, you may only need a word or two such as *for example*, or *similarly*.
- *Where do I place a transition*? You can include the transition at the end of a paragraph or at the beginning of the next.
- *What the best transition to use*? If you are stuck or unsure of the exact meaning of a word, you may want to consult the dictionary, an online writing source, or use the handy guide contained in Table 8.1.

Scrubbing

After you finish writing your ending, what's next? It's time to start scrubbing your article. What in the world is scrubbing? It's a term (tak-

TABLE 8.1. Guide to Transitions.

Relationship	Transition
Similarity	also, in the same way, just as . . . so too, likewise, similarly
Exception/contrast	but, however, in spite of, on the one hand . . . on the other hand, nevertheless, nonetheless, notwithstanding, in contrast, on the contrary, still, yet, by comparison, although, although this may be true, conversely, meanwhile
Time	after, afterward, thereafter, at last, soon, before, finally, then, currently, during, earlier, immediately, later, meanwhile, now, recently, simultaneously, subsequently, then, previously, formerly, first then second
Emphasis	Even, in fact, truly, in fact, of course
Cause and effect	accordingly, consequently, hence, so, therefore, thus, because, for, since, for the same reason, obviously, evidently, furthermore, moreover, besides, indeed, in fact, in addition, in any case, that is
Add—provide additional support or evidence— repeat	additionally, again, also, and, as well, besides, equally important, finally, further, furthermore, in addition, what's more moreover, nor, in brief, as I have said, as I have noted, as has been noted
Conclusion/summary	finally, in a word, in brief, briefly, in conclusion, in the end, in the final analysis, on the whole, thus, to conclude, to summarize, in sum, to sum up, in summary, as I have said, as I have shown, hence, therefore

Sources: Purdue 2019; UNC 2019.

en from a book on writing by Gary and Glynis Hoffman—*Adios, Struck and White*, 2003) that literally means cleaning up your manuscript. It's what the Hoffmans' call polishing your text until it shines. This process gives you the opportunity (and the fun) of refining your writing to be sure that it is the most clear and elegant as it can be.

Most experienced writers have their own scrubbing techniques. But even in this high-tech era, we think it can still be very beneficial as a way of scrubbing to print out a copy of your text, grab a red pen, and get busy scrubbing out anything that will keep you from becoming a great writer. Here's a handy scrubbing checklist that will remind you about what to remove:

- *Tangents*—This includes trimming anything that has no immediate relevance to your thesis, or any extra examples that do not add much to your work.
- *Passive voice*—Find any examples of passive voice and change them

to active. (Authors can use the review function in Word to search for examples of passive voice.) Aim to minimize or eliminate use of the any form of the verb "be."

- *Indecisive terms*—If you sounded unsure of something (kind of, sort of, or maybe), you should either remove it or rewrite it.
- *Word choice*—Listen to the words that you have selected—do they express the exact meaning you intended? Can you find a more powerful word?
- *Informalities*—Delete *all* of the following: Contractions (*can't, isn't, it's*); abbreviations (*Sun., Aug., Brit. Lit.*); colloquialisms (*What is up with that?*); idioms (*The Doubting Thomases waited until there was irrefutable proof.*); clichés (*Love is, as they say, blind.*); slang (*The scientists made one sick discovery.*); euphemisms (*She was a lady of the evening.*); offensive words (*insults, curse words, inappropriate or informal terminology*); and pronouns if they are not permitted by your style guide.
- *Wordiness*—Delete any noun strings (more than two or three nouns used to describe one thing); unnecessarily long words; and very long sentences with more than two or three clauses. As the famous writer Stephen King has advised us, "Get rid of every ounce of excess fat."

Finally, after you have finished scrubbing, put your work away for at least two days. Then, return to your narrative, and read your manuscript aloud to be sure you have scrubbed your narrative clean. Then, be brave and hand your work to a colleague for a final review.

Practice Exercises

Exercise: Changing the Voice from Passive to Active

1. A seminal study on the nursing work environment was conducted by Aiken and colleagues (2011).
2. A report on your monthly progress on the project must be submitted by the first of every month.
3. The finalization of the work plan was completed by the committee, but only after ten hours of discussion have been conducted.
4. It is the opinion of the CEO that the new personnel policy is being misinterpreted by the staff.

5. At each staff meeting, at least one new idea was identified by the participants.
6. It has been shown that the new budget process has saved the hospital money.
7. My computer has been repaired two times in the last month.
8. The report was written by an interdisciplinary team from the health institute.
9. Before the year was over, the new incentive program for top hospital executives had been approved by the Board of Trustees.
10. Later in the day, the hospital employees were informed about their loss of benefits by the director of human resources.

Exercise: Use of the Passive Voice in Writing About Research Methods

Edit this paragraph and make changes in the word choice and active vs. passive voice to improve the quality of the writing.

The researcher obtained approval to conduct the study from the Institutional Review Board (IRBs) and the Medical College, after submitting the study protocol to the human subjects review committee (Appendix A). Prior to the beginning of data collection, the researcher provided a detailed description of the project to the provost and obtained permission to use the medical school as the study site. Upon approval, she began recruitment of the subjects at an orientation meeting for new students. The researcher sent the students an invitation to participate in the study. A week after the meeting, the researcher contacted all students by phone, reviewed the eligibility criteria, and scheduled the medical students for one-to-one interviews. A standardized interview guide was used to conduct the interviews, which were held in a private office in the medical school.

The researcher recorded the fifteen interviews with the subjects' permission on her iPhone using the QuickVoice Application. These recordings were then sent electronically to a transcription service called *TranscribeMe*, that utilized an application programming interface. The researcher reviewed all transcribed interviews for accuracy by reviewing her field notes against the audio-recorded interviews. The researcher identified any obvious errors made in the transcripts and ensured that the results were reliable.

Exercise: Parallel Construction

Edit the following examples to ensure correct parallel construction.

1. Our plan is as follows:
   a. Call a meeting of all staff.
   b. Brainstorming ideas for new workshops.
   c. We should hire more writers.
   d. To update the training manuals.
2. We hired the applicant because she seemed very enthusiastic and because of her expertise in pain management.
3. To organize the hospital's holiday party, we need to do the following:
   a. A date
   b. Make a guest list
   c. Buying invitations
   d. Interview of caterers
   e. Discussion with a party planner
   f. Collect money for a gift to charity
4. Three reasons that hospitals in our area cannot find enough nurses are the competitive job market, our wages are low, and there are limited funds for professional development.
5. After reviewing all the recommendations, speaking with consultants, and having reconsidered the decision, the CEO made a surprising announcement.

Exercise: Restrictive vs. Non-Restrictive Clauses

Identify if the italicized element is restrictive or non-restrictive and add commas, where appropriate.

1. Hospitals in states *that have expanded Medicaid* have seen a decrease in the use of emergency services.
2. The human resource committee agreed to rewrite the hospital's sick policy *which was last rewritten ten years ago.*
3. Our new patient care center *which we moved to last month* does not yet have a paved parking lot for patients.
4. The chairman of the hospital board *who just moved to England* is now studying at the London School of Economics.
5. The professor Peter Senge created business concepts about organizational learning *that were viewed as revolutionary at that time.*

6. My husband *a professor at the local community college* used to work in corporate America.

7. The professional development department will supply all the materials *that are required for the continuing education course.*

8. The Affordable Care Act *which was signed into law in 2010* requires all US citizens to purchase health insurance or pay a penalty.

9. I left my son at the hospital daycare center *which is free to all full-time employees of the hospital.*

10. Dr. Jones, the request *you submitted yesterday* has been rejected by the insurance provider.

Exercise: Subject-Verb Agreement

For each example, select the correct verb.

1. Every employee and manager (has, have) received a copy of the new personnel policy.

2. The members of the committee (has, have) met to discuss the amendments to the resolution.

3. One of the administrative assistants (is, are) being replaced.

4. All of the candidates for the COO position (is, are) very qualified for the job.

5. The staff (has, have) usually received a holiday bonus in their last paycheck of the year.

6. Enclosed (is, are) copies of the monthly statements that you requested.

7. Tim is one of the specialists who (analyze, analyzes) the statistical data from the bureau.

8. Tim is the only one of the specialists who (analyzes, analyze) the statistical data.

9. Neither my assistant nor my paralegal (recalls, recall) receiving a letter about the legal case.

10. One-half of the documents (has, have) been translated into French.

11. Both the manager and the assistant manager (is, are) on vacation this month.

12. Our memo, as well as the report issued by the two companies, (was, were) offered as evidence at the hearing.

13. What the staff need (is, are) the step-by-step procedures.

Exercise: Pronoun—Antecedent Agreement

In this exercise, review each sentence and make sure that the antecedents and the pronouns agree.

1. The blue team has already passed their quota.
2. A researcher who specializes in criminal justice reform may discover that they have just begun to understand the complexities of reform.
3. When the procedures are completed, it will substantiate our claim.
4. The staff are going on their annual retreat in July.
5. The jury has rendered their verdict.
6. Someone has left his/her keys at the front reception desk.
7. The Institute is proud of their publications.
8. Everyone has completed his course evaluation survey.
9. Unanimously, the faculty expressed their dissatisfaction with the new hiring policy.
10. Neither the candidates nor the moderator did their best to answer the voters' questions.

Exercise: Who vs. Whom

Review each statement and choose either who or whom.

1. We will appoint (whoever, whomever) presents the best proposal.
2. The accountant (who, whom) I trust will file an extension for my taxes.
3. We need a manager (who, whom) understands the staffing requirement of the project.
4. John Adams is the board member (who, whom) the group was praising.
5. Abe Lincoln, (who, whom) I consider to be a great leader, negotiated a historic agreement.
6. (Who, whom) shall I say is calling?
7. John is the candidate (who, whom) we were discussing at last week's meeting.
8. Cedric has not decided (who, whom) should be appointed to the board.
9. The consultant (who, whom) you recommended is not available until January.
10. (Who, whom) left this report on my desk.

Exercise: Modifiers

Review each sentence and correct the problem with the modifiers.

1. Yesterday I counted twelve absent staff members on a walk through the office.
2. Using the company's new credit card, these problems should not come up.
3. Traffic was reported to be stalled by the police.
4. To be tender and edible, you must marinate the meat for at least four hours.
5. After searching for the lost personnel files, the files were finally found.
6. We need someone to audit reports with statistical experience.
7. While vacationing, the scientist's new book was completed.
8. After taking a long test, the faculty panel accepted me as a candidate for a graduate degree.
9. To receive a reply to our inquiry, a self-addressed, stamped envelope must be enclosed.
10. Running into a long-forgotten classmate from high school, her name escaped me completely.

Answers to Practice Exercises

Answers to Exercise: Parallel Construction

Edit the following examples to ensure correct parallel construction.

1. Our plan is as follows:
   a. Call a meeting of all staff.
   b. Brainstorming ideas for new workshops.
   c. We should hire more writers.
   d. To update the training manuals.

   We plan to call a staff meeting, brainstorm ideas for new workshops, and consider hiring more writers to update the training manuals.

2. We hired the applicant because she seemed very enthusiastic and because of her expertise in pain management.

   We hired the new applicant because of her expertise in pain management and her enthusiastic attitude.

3. To organize the hospital's holiday party, we need to do the following:
   a. A date
   b. Make a guest list
   c. Buying invitations
   d. Interview of caterers
   e. Discussion with a party planner
   f. Collect money for a gift to charity

   Organizing the hospital's holiday party requires identifying a date, discussing the event with a party planner, creating a guest list, purchasing invitations, interviewing caterers, and collecting money for a gift to charity.

4. Three reasons that hospitals in our area cannot find enough nurses are the competitive job market, our wages are low, and there are limited funds for professional development.

   Area hospitals cannot find enough nurses because of the competitive job market, low wages, and limited funds for professional development.

5. After reviewing all the recommendations, speaking with consultants, and having reconsidered the decision, the CEO made a surprising announcement.

   The CEOs made a surprising announcement after reconsidering the decision and speaking with consultants.

Answers to Exercise: Restrictive vs. Non-restrictive Clauses

Identify if the italicized element is restrictive (R) or non-restrictive (NR), and add commas where appropriate.

1. Hospitals in states *that have expanded Medicaid* have seen a decrease in the use of emergency services. **R**

2. The human resource committee agreed to rewrite the hospital's sick policy, *which was last rewritten 10 years ago.* **NR**

3. Our new patient care center, *which we moved to last month*, does not yet have a paved parking lot for patients. **NR**

4. The chairman of the hospital board, *who just moved to England*, is now studying at the London School of Economics. **NR**

5. The professor Peter Senge created business concepts about organizational learning *that were viewed as revolutionary at that time.* **R**

6. My husband, *a professor at the local community college*, used to work in corporate America. **NR**

7. The professional development department will supply all the materials *that are required for the continuing education course.* **R**

8. The Affordable Care Act, *which was signed into law in 2010*, requires all US citizens to purchase health insurance or pay a penalty. **NR**

9. I left my son at the hospital daycare center *which is free to all full-time employees of the hospital.* **NR**

10. Dr. Jones, the request *that you submitted yesterday* has been rejected by the insurance provider. **R**

Answers to Exercise: Subject-verb Agreement

For each example, select the correct verb.

1. Every employee and manager (**has**, have) received a copy of the new personnel policy.

2. The members of the committee (has, **have**) met to discuss the amendments to the resolution.

3. One of the administrative assistants (**is**, are) being replaced.

4. All of the candidates for the COO position (is, **are**) very qualified for the job.

5. The staff (**has**, **have**) usually received a holiday bonus in their last paycheck of the year.

6. Enclosed (is, **are**) copies of the monthly statements that you requested.

7. Tim is one of the specialists who (**analyze**, analyzes) the statistical data from the bureau.

8. Tim is the only one of the specialists who (**analyzes**, analyze) the statistical data.

9. Neither my assistant nor my paralegal (**recalls**, recall) receiving a letter about the legal case.

10. One-half of the documents (has, **have**) been translated into French.

11. Both the manager and the assistant manager (is, **are**) on vacation this month.

12. Our memo, as well as the report issued by the two companies, (**was**, were) offered as evidence at the hearing.

13. What the staff need (is, **are**) the step-by-step procedures.

Answers to Exercise: Pronoun—Antecedent Agreement

In this exercise, review each sentence and make sure that the antecedents and the pronouns agree (A) or does not agree (DNA).

1. The blue team has already passed their quota. **A**
2. A researcher who specializes in criminal justice reform may discover that they have just begun to understand the complexities of reform. **DNA**
3. When the procedures are completed, it will substantiate our claim. **DNA**
4. The staff are going on their annual retreat in July. **A**
5. The jury has rendered their verdict. **DNA**
6. Someone has left his/her keys at the front reception desk. **A**
7. The Institute is proud of their publications. **DNA**
8. Everyone has completed his course evaluation survey. **A**
9. Unanimously, the faculty expressed their dissatisfaction with the new hiring policy. **A**
10. Neither the candidates nor the moderator did their best to answer the voters' questions. **A**

Answers to Exercise: Who vs. whom

Review each statement and choose either who or whom.

1. We will appoint (whoever, **whomever**) presents the best proposal.
2. The accountant (**who**, whom) I trust will file an extension for my taxes.
3. We need a manager (**who**, whom) understands the staffing requirement of the project.
4. John Adams is the board member (who, **whom**) the group was praising.
5. Abe Lincoln, (**who**, whom) I consider to be a great leader, negotiated a historic agreement.
6. (Who, **whom**) shall I say is calling?
7. John is the candidate (**who**, whom) we were discussing at last week's meeting.
8. Cedric has not decided (**who**, whom) should be appointed to the board.

9. The consultant (who, **whom**) you recommended is not available until January.

10. (**Who**, whom) left this report on my desk.

Answers to Exercise: Modifiers

Review each sentence and correct the problem with the modifiers.

1. Yesterday I counted twelve absent staff members on a walk through the office.

   As I walked through the office yesterday, I noticed twelve absent staff members.

2. Using the company's new credit card, these problems should not come up.

   These problems should not occur when we use the company's new credit card.

3. Traffic was reported to be stalled by the police.

   The police stalled the flow of traffic.

4. To be tender and edible, you must marinate the meat for at least four hours

   For meat to be tender and edible, it must be marinated for at least four hours.

5. After searching for the lost personnel files, the files were finally found.

   Diligent searching finally produced the lost personnel files.

6. We need someone to audit reports with statistical experience.

   We need someone with statistical experience to audit the reports.

7. While vacationing, the scientist's new book was completed.

   The scientist completed the new book while she was on vacation.

8. After taking a long test, the faculty panel accepted me as a candidate for a graduate degree.

   After taking a long test, the faulty panel accepted me as a candidate for graduate degree.

9. To receive a reply to our inquiry, a self-addressed, stamped envelope must be enclosed.

   Enclose is a self-addressed, stamped envelope for your reply.

10. Running into a long-forgotten classmate from high school, her name escaped me completely.

    When I ran into a long-forgotten high school classmate, I couldn't remember her name.

Your Writing Assignment

The best writing comes from rewriting. It has been said that great writers devote more time to rewriting than they do to writing their first draft. So, as you work toward becoming a great writer, here is a great opportunity.

1. Select an article or report that you have authored. This can be a journal article, a technical report, a white paper, or another type of scientific or technical publication.
2. Set aside time in your work/personal schedule to work on this writing assignment.
3. Retrieve a Word document with the final copy of your article. You will use this as your new working draft.
4. Review the scrubbing checklist and begin scrubbing the content. This means that you will make a number of changes. Please use track changes.
5. Re-visit the beginning of your article. Do you think this captured the readers' interest? Did it set the stage for rest of the content? How could you improve it?
6. Analyze your word choices. Have you chosen the best words to express your thoughts? What words would have been better?
7. Next, look at the structure of the article. Are the main points easy to identify and arranged in a logical order? Do all the sub-points answer questions about the main points? Do paragraphs have no more than eight lines? Does the article flow?
8. Reflect on the tone of your article. Did the tone accurately reflect your attitude toward the subject, the subject, and the publication? What changes would you make?
9. Re-visit the ending of your article. Did you answer the important questions: "So what? Now what?"
10. Please keep notes as you move through this reflective yet practical exercise. Note new insights, and challenges. Record the changes you made to your original article. As time permits,

re-write as many sections as you can. Then go back and compare the before and after article. You should be pleased with your progress.

References

Allen, S. 2019. "Who vs. Whom." https://www.grammarly.com/blog/who-vs-whom-its-not-as-complicated-as-you-might-think/.

American Psychological Association. 2010. *Publication Manual of the American Psychological Association*. (6th ed.) Washington, DC, USA: The American Psychological Association.

Cerejo, C. 2013. "Using the Active and Passive Voice in Research Writing." https://doi.org/10.34193/EI-A-5200.

Creigton, K. 2018. "Why is Parallel Structure Important in Writing?" https://www.proofreadnow.com/blog/why-is-parallel-structure-important-in-writing.

Hoffman, G. and G. Hoffman. 2003. *Adios, Struck and White*. (3rd ed.) Huntington Beach, CA, USA: Verve Press.

Kennedy, M. S. 2014. "Getting Writing Right." *Am J Nursing* 114 (3), 7. http://journals.lww.com/ajnonline/Fulltext/2014/03000/Getting_Writing_Right.1.aspx.

Lumen Learning. 2019a. "Modifiers: Adjectives and adverbs." Retrieved from https://courses.lumenlearning.com/boundless-writing/chapter/modifiers-adjectives-and-adverbs/

Lumen Learning, 2019b. "Use parallel structure." Retrieved from https://courses.lumenlearning.com/technicalwriting/chapter/use-paraellel-structure-2/

Luo, A. 2019. "Using parallelism to write balanced sentences." Retrieved from https://www.scribbr.com/language-rules/parallelism/

Nichol, M. 2012. "5 types of misplaced modifiers: A modifier's placement in a sentence can skew your meaning." Retrieved from https://www.ragan.com/5-types-of-misplaced-modifiers/

Purdue University. 2019. "Purdue Online Writing Lab—Making subjects and verbs agree." Retrieved from https://owl.purdue.edu/owl/general_writing/grammar/subject_verb_agreement.html

Strunk, W., Jr., and E. B. White. 2009. *The Elements of Style*. (50th Anniversary Edition). New York, USA: Pearson Longman.

Trafiss, C. 2019. "Restrictive and Nonrestrictive Clauses: What's the difference?" Retrieved from https://www.grammarly.com/blog/using-that-and-which-is-all-about-restrictive-and-non-restrictive-clauses/

University of North Carolina Writing Center (UNC). 2019. "Transitions." Retrieved from https://writingcenter.unc.edu/tips-and-tools/transitions/

University of Wisconsin Writing Center. 2019. "Use the active voice." Retrieved from https://writing.wisc.edu/handbook/style/ccs_activevoice/

Williams, J.M. and Bizup, J. 2014. *Style: Lessons in clarity and grace*. Upper Saddle River, NJ, USA: Pearson Education, Inc.

SECTION IV

CHAPTER 9

Techniques to Immediately Improve Writing Rigor

There's something marvelously satisfying with finishing a draft,
no matter how bad it is. Now I can go to work. Before, the piece
of writing was all idea and vision, hope and possibility,
a mist. Now it is ink on paper, and I can work it.
—Donald Murray 1980

Introduction

SINCE the 2010 Institute of Medicine Report called for doubling the number of nurses with a doctorate degree by 2020, universities nationwide now focus on developing doctoral nursing programs. The impressive growth in programs illustrated in Figure 9.1 demonstrates the result of nursing programs expanding traditional PhD doctoral education to the evidence-based Doctor of Nursing Practice (DNP) degree.

The impressive findings from the 2018 American Association of Colleges of Nursing (AACN) survey illustrated in Figure 9.2 demonstrate the significant growth in both PhD and DNP doctoral programs and explains why faculty hasten to respond to nurses' newfound interest in obtaining terminal degrees (AACN 2019).

At the beginning of each new academic year, faculty welcome a growing number of nurses into graduate programs. These new students eagerly join on-campus or online class cohorts, access class lectures and discussions, and proceed to completing their first writing assignment. These new graduate students fully expect their submissions to easily meet the course requirements. Professors review, score, and return assignments to students who expect to receive an A grade, but receive a C grade instead. In one scenario, a student, devastated by the C grade, reviews the professor's comments, which indicate that poor writing contributed significantly to the student's low score. The professor invites the student to re-submit the assignment after re-writing it.

In another scenario, a nurse writer submits a manuscript to a peer-

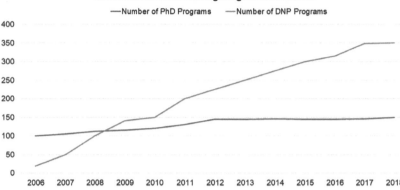

Figure 9.1. Growth in Doctoral Nursing Programs: 2006–2018. Adapted from: AACN 2019.

reviewed journal for publication. A rejection letter details shortfalls in the submission, which center on writing weaknesses, but also applauds the article's content, depth, and potential contribution to the field of nursing. An editor invites the author to re-submit the manuscript within a relatively short period of time.

What should the student and the nurse writer do? How might an immediate writing transformation take place in such a short period of time? This chapter offers proven methods to immediately transform one's writing style to a level closer to the rigor expected in graduate school and by journal editorial boards: use of active, not passive voice, and elimination of "be" verbs.

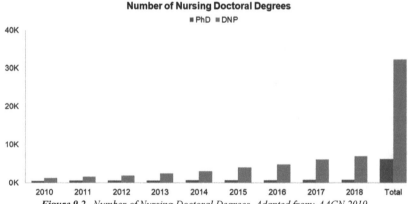

Figure 9.2. Number of Nursing Doctoral Degrees. Adapted from: AACN 2019.

Passive vs. Active Voice

While content in Chapter 8 included defining passive and active voice, we further emphasize its importance in achieving graduate level writing rigor in this chapter. Students who consistently write in the active voice are more likely to develop concise, clear and more forcible narratives indicative of subject matter expertise. (Shrunk and White 2000).

Refreshing your understanding, active voice focuses on the action of the subject in a sentence, whereas passive voice uses the subject as the object of the action (Blinn College 2018; CopyPress 2018). As shown in Figure 9.3, the action of the subject is the most important factor in the relationship to the action.

Using active voice throughout a manuscript clarifies the meaning for the reader and decreases wordiness and lack of clarity, whereas overuse of the passive voice diminishes the intent or meaning of the sentence (Purdue OWL 2019; Laser 2015; Strunk and White 2000). Sentences with active voice generally use fewer words than those that use passive voice, as noted in the examples below:

Passive Voice:

Revisions were initiated and an outline was created to assist in creating a solid framework for this paper.

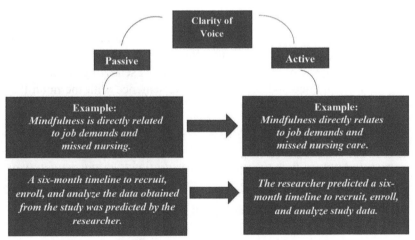

Figure 9.3. Passive and Active Voices.

Active Voice:

Revisions included developing a manuscript outline to guide framework development.

Passive Voice:

Upon completion of the observation phase, nurses on the pediatric floor were given a one-month timeframe to complete an online training tool that was developed by the National Institutes of Health entitled "Continuing Education Program on SIDS Risk Reduction."

Active Voice:

Following completion of the observation phase, a one-month timeframe enabled nurses on the pediatric floor to complete an NIH-developed online training tool entitled "Continuing Education Program on SIDS Risk Reduction."

Passive Voice:

My first class in graduate school will always be remembered for its focus on improving my writing proficiency.

Active Voice:

I will always remember my first class in graduate school because it focused on writing proficiency improvement.

Tips for Moving from Active to Passive Voice

Tips for revising sentences from passive to active voice include reversing the order of subject-object. Begin the sentence with the object, transforming it into the subject and selecting a strong verb to connect it to the new subject. Another technique involves searching for the word "by" in the sentence and restructuring the sentence with the noun that follows the word "by" (Blinn College 2018), as shown below.

- Change *"It has been suggested by physicians that nurses are not qualified to function independently as APNs"* to *"Physicians suggest that nurses lack the qualifications to function independently as APNs."*

An additional tip involves the use of general terms, particularly when discussing research findings. Use the general reference term when the sentence subject is not known (Blinn College, 2018). For example,

- Change *"Potential study subjects were invited to participate using the institution's email system"* to *"Researchers invited potential study participants using the institution's email system."*

The consistent use of the active voice enhances the force, and perceived importance, of writing (Shrunk and White 2000). By strengthening the sentence and shortening its length, the writer heightens the rigor as well. Rigor in graduate school programs is essential because it represents masters and doctoral level work (Goodman, Robert and Johnson 2020). Rigor in writing articles for publication increase the acceptance of manuscript in peer-reviewed journals (Saver, 2014). Journal editors respond positively to manuscript submissions that use active voice, because active voice imparts the writer's confidence in mastery of the topic (Johnson and Rulo 2019; Goodman, Robert and Johnson 2020).

Eliminate Use of "Be" Verbs

To use the active voice, the writer must reorganize sentences. In this process, the writer focuses on the most important writing tool of all—verbs (Zinsser 2006). However, writers often rely far too heavily on use of "be" verbs rather than choosing stronger verbs or re-writing sentences in the active voice. Writers must remember that all forms of the "be" verb suggests weakness, emit less confidence, and diminish rigor. Writers who avoid their use of this weak verb inevitably produce a better structured sentence and stronger, more confident statement (Dialogue Workshop 2011; Pennington 2009; Printwand Staff 2008; Radley 2018). In addition, writers should avoid using the "be" verb when expressing the future tense as well, such as *"The participants will be trying to complete the survey during work hours."* Instead, writers should switch to the active voice and replace the "be" verb with a stronger verb: *"Completion of the participant survey will take place during work hours."* The second sentence imparts strength, greater confidence, and clear intent.

Harris (2015) found that in forcing students to eliminate the use of "be" verbs in class assignments, the process "often fixed many of the (problematic) issues I would identify in their papers," such as run-on sentences, unclear subjects, and poor sentence structure (2). Replacing "be" verbs also helps improve writing rigor in four ways (Blinn College 2018): first, by clarifying and making the claim in a sentence more understandable; second, by eliminating redundant information contained in a sentence; third, by searching for a stronger verb and expanding the writer's vocabulary; and fourth, by injecting energy into writing. As writers select stronger verbs and stop using weak linking verbs or copulatives, the writer's writing range expands and moves closer toward the expected level of rigor, an attribute that is sought by journal editors and graduate program academicians alike.

How to Eliminate Using "Be" Verbs

Learning how to replace weak verbs requires focus and hard work (Radley 2018). The steep learning curve can test the most engaged writer. But what reads better: *"The evidence was sufficient to modify practice by creating a foundation."* or *"The evidence generated a sufficient foundation to modify practice?"* The following steps can assist writers to move away from relying heavily on "be" verbs (Blinn College 2018):

- *Step 1*: Develop the first draft of a manuscript without focusing on eliminating "be" verbs or weak copulatives.
- *Step 2*: Identify the "be" verbs. Print out and circle or highlight all forms of the verb "be" evident in the draft manuscript. Hint: Use Microsoft Word's find function to move the process along more quickly.
- *Step 3*: Determine if removing the "be" verb is unavoidable. Ask: does the "be" verb help another verb thereby relating a sense of timing such as *"I am working very hard to complete this difficult assignment."*
- *Step 4*: If the "be" verb aids another verb ending in "ed," such as "was completed" or any irregular verb such as "we removed," change the sentence to the active voice. Example: *"I completed my work before we removed the sign."*
- *Step 5*: If the verb "be" function in linking a subject to a word that describes the subject, replace it with a stronger verb. Example: Change *"The editor's comments were brutal but accurate."* to *"The editor offered brutal but accurate comments."*

TABLE 9.1. *"Be" Verbs to Eliminate.*

is, am, are, was, were, be, being, been, will, would, may, might, must, can, could, has been, have been, had been, could be, should be, would be, will be, might be, must be, can be, was being, were being

Adapted from: Moxley 2018; St. Louis Community College n.d.; Pennington 2009.

- *Step 6*: Replace "be" verbs with stronger verbs. For instance, *"Here is the student's dissertation for professor review."* Substitute the "be" verb as follows: *"The professor readies to review the student's dissertation."* Table 9.1 offers a list of many forms of the verb "be" that writers writers should avoid (Moxley 2018; St. Louis Community College n.d.; Pennington 2009).
- *Step 7*: Change from passive to active voice when the sentence contains a form of the "be" verb. Select strong verbs. Hint: Use Microsoft Word's synonym finder. Over time, the writer's vocabulary will also improve (Dialogue Workshop 2011; Johnson, Goodman, and Robert 2020).

Since experts have described "be" verbs as somewhat lifeless and vague, removing them enables the writer to change the sentence structure and insert adjectives and adverbs that more fully explain the writer's thinking (Pennington 2009; Radley 2018). Instead of, *"Reusing my drafts is something I really hate to do, but I do it because my professor is not happy otherwise,"* try, *"I dislike revising my drafts, but I understand the importance of strengthening my work and improving clarity, logic, and flow."*

Finally, as writers select stronger verbs and depart from using weak verbs, the writer's proficiency range expands and moves closer toward the expected level of graduate school and publication rigor. Remember, writing standards emphasize using strong verbs; avoiding weak verbs, including all forms of the "be" verb, such as *is, was,* and *are*; and opting for stronger, more assertive verbs, such as *emphasizes, appears,* and *regulates* (Johnson and Rulo 2018; Johnson *et al.* 2020; Pennington 2009).

Transformative Examples

The following two examples illustrate the effectiveness of using the active voice and eliminating use of "be" verbs.

Before: The procedure of conducting research at the institution of The Catholic University of America is a process that starts with ascertaining whether or not the research requires an Institutional Review Board (IRB). The university is adamant that all proposals which involve human subjects require an IRB approval. In addition, special protections are granted to minors, prisoners, pregnant women, and vulnerable populations. The principal investigator (PI) is expected to complete an ethics certification course online. The instructor can require that students complete the CITI training, but it makes no sense to do that until the student is ready and has completed the research proposal. CITI training is an on-line program that is lengthy and takes a long time to complete.

After: The Catholic University of America requires all university researchers to apply to and receive approval from the CUA Institutional Review Board (IRB). The university enforces this requirement to ensure human subjects' protection. In compliance with Federal law, the university grants special protection to minors, prisoners, pregnant women, and vulnerable populations. In addition, the university expects the principal investigator to successfully complete an on-line ethics program and a series of CITI training modules prior to applying for IRB project review.

Before: To sum up, gaining a PhD degree in Nursing is my true dream. It adds special meaning and excitement to my life, and with high anticipation, I'm in the processes of working on that goal. I'm saying that because I firmly believe that patients and their families and our communities deserve to receive more than what we can provide today. Also, I can add something to my profession. I can do something more even if no one else sees that I can. It is possible to see my dream as a reality.

After: I look forward to gaining my PhD degree in nursing. I envision that the exciting journey will enrich my professional life, and I anticipate that my newfound knowledge will better support my patients, their families and the communities I serve. Further, achieving my dream includes my commitment to enrich and advance my profession.

This chapter provided two techniques that can immediately improve writing proficiency. The use of the active voice rather than the passive voice and the reduction in and/or elimination of "be" verbs can assist writers in elevating writing skill sets and improve clarity, logic, and flow. Although the process requires focus and hard work, the net result far outweighs the effort.

Practice Exercises

Part A: Converting Sentences from Passive to Active Voice

The following five sentences reflect use of the passive voice. Based on the content in this chapter, restructure the sentences to reflect the active voice.

1. The research is supported by an enormous amount of evidence that gives the principal investigator the foundation needed to support the research.

2. The evidence-based practice project was developed and tested in a multi-system healthcare organization, which made implementation difficult.

3. The authors of the manuscript were saddened with the editor's decision but they decided that they would re-write the article, re-submit, and hope for the best.

4. The student was telling the professors when she could be available for an on-line Zoom session to review her assignment.

5. The article's author is well known and does a great deal of publishing, so she knows what editors prefer.

Part B: Eliminate the "Be" Verbs in the Following Ten Sentences

1. It is my intention to transfer to a university that offers a streamlined DNP program since my on-campus program is too time-consuming.

2. There were some important findings from research I did for my dissertation.

3. The disease process can be devastating, but with new treatments, patients are hopeful and their nurses are hopeful too.

4. I was interested in reading the research, but I could not apply it to my work setting because the organization would not support it.

5. The American Academy of Nursing is expecting knowledge dissemination from nurses who have gotten advanced degrees.

6. She will be able to finish her degree if she enrolls right away in an on-line program.

7. The author will be permitted to re-submit the article, but she has a very narrow window of opportunity.

8. Three nurses on my unit are going to attend the state university next semester.

9. The American Association for Nurse Practitioners has been very supportive of nurses seeking a DNP or PhD degree, but reminds them of their expertise in advanced practice nursing.

10. There is the road to achievement and here are the obstacles which must be overcome.

References

AACN (American Association of Colleges of Nursing). 2019. "Fact Sheet: The Doctor of Nursing Practice." https://www.aacnnursing.org/Portals/42/News/Factsheets/DNP-Factsheet.pdf.

AACN (American Association of Colleges of Nursing). 2019. "Number of people receiving nursing doctoral degrees annually." https://campaignforaction.org/resource/number-people-receiving-nursing-doctoral-degrees-annually/.

Blinn College. 2018. "Reducing 'be' verbs in writing." Retrieved from https://www.copypress.com/blog/importance-active-voice-content/

Dialogue Workshop. 2011. "Writing without the verb 'to be': A useful conversation technique." Retrieved from https://www.dailykos.com/stories/2011/3/25/960073/-

Goodman, P., Robert, R. C. & Johnson, J.E. (2020). Rigor in PhD dissertation research. *Nursing Forum*. 1–10. https://doi.org/10.1111/nuf.12477

Harris, M. 2015. "Why I declared war on be verbs." Retrieved from http://higheredprofessor.com/2015/11/19/why-i-declared-war-on-be-verbs/

IOM (Institute of Medicine). 2010. *The Future of Nursing: Leading Change, Advancing Health.* http://www.nationalacademies.org/hmd/Reports/2010/The-Future-of-Nursing-Leading-Change-Advancing-Health.aspx.

Laser, M. 2015. "Novelist teaches freshman writing, is shocked by students' inability to construct basic sentences." Retrieved from https://hechingerreport.org/novelist-teaches-freshman-writing-is-shocked-by-students-inability-to-construct-basic-sentences/

Moxley, J. 2018. "Eliminate 'to be' verbs." Retrieved from https://writingcommons.org/open-text/style/sentence-structure/101-eliminate-to-be-verbs

Murray, Donald 1980. *The feel of writing and teaching writing.* In *Reinventing the Rhetorical Tradition.* A. Freedman and I. Pringle (eds). Urbana, IL, USA: National Council of Teachers.

Pennington. M. 2009. "How to eliminate 'to be' verbs in writing." Retrieved from https://blog.penningtonpublishing.com/grammar_mechanics/how-to-eliminate-to-be-verbs-in-writing/

Purdue University 2019. "Active versus passive voice." Retrieved from https://owl.purdue.edu/owl/general_writing/academic_writing/active_and_passive_voice/active_versus_passive_voice.html

Printwand Staff. 2012. "How to eliminate 'to be' verbs in business writing." Retrieved from https://www.printwand.com/blog/how-to-eliminate-to-be-verbs-in-business-writing

Radley, G. 2018. "Not to be: Removing *be* verbs from your writing." Retrieved from https://www.writermag.com/improve-your-writing/revision-grammar/not-removing-verbs-writing/

Saver, C. 2014. *Anatomy of writing for publication for nurses.* (2nd ed.). Indianapolis, IN, USA: Sigma Theta Tau.

Strunk, W., and White, E. B. 2000. (4th ed.) *The elements of style.* Upper Saddle River, NJ, USA: Pearson Education, Inc

St. Louis Community College. n.d. "*To be* or not *to be*: Replacing to be verbs." Retrieved from https://www.stlcc.edu/docs/student-support/academic-support/college-writing-center/to-be-verbs.pdf

Williams, J. M., and Bizup, J. 2014. *Style: Lessons in clarity and grace.* (11th ed.) Upper Saddle River, NJ, USA: Pearson Education, Inc.

Zinsser, W.K. 2006. *On writing well.* New York. NY, USA: Harper Collins Publishers.

CHAPTER 10

Word Choice: A Strategic Imperative

Short words are best and the old words when short are best of all.
—Winston Churchill

Introduction

WITH one million words in the English language, writers have an enormous list of possibilities. Such a wide choice! What word is best and how does the writer choose? Word selection significantly affects the quality of any manuscript, and its importance cannot be overstated. As a subject matter expert, the writer's job is to convey content that the writer knows well and the reader does not. Selecting the wrong word or wrong form of a word can confuse a reader because a narrative requires clear, concise expression. This chapter addresses word choice as an important consideration for writers and offers suggestions to align the selection of words with the writer's intended message.

Accurate Word Selection

Vocabulary includes words that denote *function*, and others that denote *content* (Pennell 2001; Tips on Choosing the Right Words, n.d.). Functional words include "are, "to" and "that" and are intended to suggest some level of action. Content words are nouns, verbs, adjectives, and adverbs that are concrete such as *recidivism* or abstract such as *holistic*. Words can also be categorized into those used for the general population and words largely reserved for specialty areas, such as sciences and professions, including nursing.

The first step in selecting words is to identify the words the writer associates with the manuscript under development. For example, when writing journal articles, the editorial guidelines usually ask the author to provide a list of key words or phrases that reflect the article's content. This list can guide the writer and keep the content on track in the major components of the manuscript. In developing this list, it is important to avoid uncommon words, which only confuse the reader. Consider this illustrative example: "Understanding the complexities of the healthcare industry today includes appreciating the nuances of white water, the challenges of gray rhinos, and the unpredictability of black swans." Unless the reader is familiar with "water, gray rhinos and black swans," the writer has not advanced the reader's understanding of the manuscript's content.

The next step is to review traditional missteps experienced by all authors—from the novice to the most seasoned writer. A common mistake is the unintended (and embarrassing) misuse of words as demonstrated in the following examples:

- "As the *principle* investigator, she intended to complete her research in one month, but the task proved too complex."
- "The article discussed an evidence-based practice project that involved addressing food *desserts* in disadvantaged neighborhoods."
- "In attempting to engage online students, the professor provided student *excess* to weekly virtual discussion sessions."
- "In researching the *elicit* drug market in the local community, the APRN easily amassed sufficient data to interest politicians and *enquire* law enforcement to develop effective strategies to address the problem."

Each of the above sentences contains an error in word choice. Table 10.1 contains a sample of these commonly confused words (Wyrick 2016, 159; Writing Explained, n.d.; Vappingo, n.d.). In each example,

TABLE 10.1. *Examples of Commonly Confused Words.*

access/excess	led/lead	accept/except
adsorb/absorb	affect/effect	illusion/allusion
advice/advise	good/well	farther/further
since/because	lose/loose	than/then
between/among	lay/lie	aloud/out loud
bi-weekly/semi-weekly	ambiance/ambience	attain/obtain
revenge/avenge	elicit/illicit	fewer/less
implicit/explicit	incident/incidence	stank/stunk
mute/moot	resume/assume	toward/towards

Adapted from: University of Richmond, n.d.; Ashford University, n.d.

TABLE 10.2. Examples of Commonly Confused Homophones.

it's/its	sight/site/cite	choose/chose
to/too/two	whose/who's	counsel/council
there/their/they're	ensure/insure	rain/reign
your/you're	adaptor/adapter	precede/proceed
compliment/complement	breech/beach	discrete/discreet
stationery/stationary	conscience/conscious	fair/fare
capitol/capital	dam/damn	flyer/flier
principal/principle	disc/disk	grey/gray
heel/heal	lens/lense	herd/heard
passed/past	peal/peel	plain/plane
road/rode	rite/right	tenets/tenants
soar/sore	threw/through/thru	borne/born

Adapted from: University of Richmond, n.d.; Vappingo, n.d.; Writing Explained, n.d.

the two words have very different meanings. To avoid any reader confusion, *always* check the accuracy of the words you have selected. Use of a dictionary or synonym finder and/or a thesaurus can assist writers to better express themselves and minimize or avoid word usage error. Many writers also use Microsoft Word's synonym checker to confirm the correct word selection.

Another area that results in errors is the incorrect use of homophones, which are words that sound the same, although the spelling and meaning differ, such as "sight," "site," and "cite," or "compliment" vs. "complement." Table 10.2 provides examples of commonly confused homophones.

Learning New Words

Writers and readers—novice to expert—benefit from expanding their vocabularies (Alingod 2014). Some general guidelines for learning new vocabulary include using a new word in written material, learning correct pronunciation through online applications, and using the new word in discussions.

Learning the root or base words can help you to retain a recently-learned word and paraphrasing the definition of a new word can also prove helpful in learning, retaining, and using the word in written or oral material (Alingod 2014; Tips on Choosing the Right Words, n.d.). An example is learning the word "bitcoin" and paraphrasing it as "digital bank-free money" to remember its meaning (Pressley, Levin, and McDaniel 1987, cited in Baumann and Kameenui 1991, 618). In addition, WordGenius.com and Dictionary.com send a word-of-the-day to each subscriber's email and offer daily follow-up quizzes to engage those interested in expanding their vocabulary. Finally, an age-old tool that inevitably develops vocabulary still can be found in newspapers, articles, and books—crossword puzzles (Alingod 2014). While challenging at times, the effort forces a person to search his/her memory to re-learn old words or appreciate new ones.

Diction and Syntax

Diction refers to the choice and use of words selected by a writer, "especially with regard to correctness, clearness, or effectiveness" (Merriam-Webster, n.d., 1). Writers usually choose a pattern of words that may seem stronger than others, such as selecting "forward" and "advancement" (School Wires, n.d.). The writer's word selection or pattern may be repeated in an effort to amplify a point to the reader as illustrated in the following example:

- "HRSA provides funds for *eligible* health professions and nursing schools for use in assisting *disadvantaged* students who demonstrate *financial* need. Interested *eligible* applicants who qualify as fund administrators are invited to submit an application. The application requires that *eligible* fund administrators demonstrate the size of the *disadvantaged* student pool envisioned to benefit from *financial* aid."

Diction also depends on "subject, purpose, and audience" (School Wires, n.d., 1). The subject determines how complex the word needs to be and if a specialized language applies, such as *evidence-based, linear, sustainability*, and *univariate* in nursing science. Diction also reflects the writer's purpose—to engage, persuade, or inform. In academic writing and in writing for publications, the reader generally expects candid and direct diction, written with a clinical tone. The audience affects the author's diction or word selection when writing for a highly educated audience, which is commonly expected in academia and in journal publications. Microsoft Word offers a reading ease and grade level analyses for authors to determine if their writing matches the anticipated reading and educational level of the intended audience. Authors should consider aiming for a rigorous reading ease score of 30 or lower, and a grade level of 15 or above. Table 10.3 offers examples of words that writers use to describe the type of diction used in developing a manuscript (School Wires, n.d.).

TABLE 10.3. *Diction Descriptive Terms or Types.*

abstract	inflammatory	scholarly	vague
academic	insincere	subdued	literal
ambiguous	learned	symbolic	ordinary
biting	obscure	technical	passionate
brusque	offensive	unifying	political
caustic	connotative	formal	pretentious
concrete	divisive	emotional	figurative

Adapted from: School Wires, n.d.; Ashford University, n.d.

Syntax refers to the way in which an author joins words together in phrases, clauses, and sentences. The manner in which this is done creates a rhythm, and ultimately the tone of the manuscript (Zinsser 2006). Word repetition, as previously discussed, enables the writer to maintain the reader's attention on an important aspect of the narrative. However, a well-developed manuscript strategically crafts and disperses long and short sentences by first, forcing the reader to "combine many thoughts into one (long) sentence (and stretch) their capacity to understand the tangible and abstract elements of the sentence" (School Wires, n.d., 6). In contrast, a short sentence can "stand out when it is unique from the sentences around it" (School Wires, n.d., 6), as illustrated in the following example (Molle 2019, 3):

- "The researchers calculated the productivity loss based on a population attributable fraction cost approach of mortality rates (Ding *et al.* 2016). Although a search failed to identify costs associated with the specific concept of sedentary behavior, the studies by Ding *et al.* (2016) and Carlson *et al.* (2015) verify the staggering costs associated with limited physical activity and sedentary behavior. *More importantly, this behavior also poses untoward health outcomes.*"

As the example illustrates, the writer focuses attention on the final short sentence—it stands apart from the others, isolating the idea it conveys, and elevating its importance.

Using Too Many Words When Few Will Do

The hallmark of an effective writer is the ability to relate content in as few words as possible (Washington University Faculty, n.d.; Zinsser, 2016). Quality writers use direct, straightforward language and strive to shorten and simplify sentences by rephrasing them to eliminate excess words. Zinsser (2016) offers a technique that involves the writer "bracketing superfluous words" (16), which enables the writer to objectively assess their relevance and/or importance to the narrative. Zinsser (2016) also suggests that writers should aim to "prune ruthlessly" (16). Strunk and White (2000) suggest that "vigorous writing is concise" (23), which does not involve writing just short sentences. Instead, make every word "tell" or be used for a specific reason. Several common expressions illustrate the problem: "the reason why is that"—"the question as to whether"—and "owing to the fact"—each of these weaken a sentence, confuse, and interrupt the rhythm of a simplified thought (Strunk and White 2000, 23–24). Consider the following example that illustrates a painfully constructed wordy sentence:

- "Before a DNP-prepared nurse makes a decision about implementing an evidence-based practice project and its related procedures, and prior to addressing the obvious organizational impact, the nurse should carefully assess, ponder and evaluate all of the practice change nuances including bedside nurse engagement."

Significant trimming, word reduction, and centering on the most important aspect of the sentence leads to the following revision:

- "Prior to implementing an evidenced-based practice change, the DNP-prepared nurse conducts an organizational assessment and engages bedside nurses to ensure project success."

The result is a clear, concise sentence devoid of wordiness or relating too much and unnecessary information.

Avoiding Clichés

As George Orwell (1946) aptly stated about using clichés, "Never use a metaphor, smile, or other figure of speech which you are used to seeing in print" (1). A cliché is a stale, overused phrase that has lost its impact (Lepki 2019). Lepki (2019) suggests that clichés are "what you write when you don't have the energy or inspiration to think of a new way to express an idea" (1). Orwell (2016) describes them as dying metaphors because writers fail to invent new phrases to use. Table 10.4 provides examples of clichés used in everyday language. They have no place in academic writing or in professional publications. Avoid their use.

TABLE 10.4. Examples of Clichés.

read between the lines	here we go again	low-hanging fruit
better safe than sorry	dead as a doornail	having said that
that went well	think outside the box	a bolt from the blue
ignorance is bliss	on the cutting edge	but at the end of the day
avoid it like the plague	thick as thieves	plenty of fish in the sea
take the tiger by the tail	all for one and one for all	if only walls could talk
the pot calling the kettle black	in the nick of time	every dog has its day
play your cards right	it's an uphill battle	can't win for losing

Adapted from: Lepki 2019; ProWriting Aid, n.d.

Overuse of "Big" Words

Word choice and diction take on new meanings when writers select words that are overly complex. Since effective writers express their
message using as few words as possible and construct phrases and sentences that are direct and to-the-point, struggling writers may overuse
"big" words in an attempt to convey sophistication and knowledge. We
refer to these stressed writers as "sesquipedalian," or someone who
loves long words (vocabulary.com). Sesquipedalian writers attempt to
impart intelligence and an expertise that may not exist. Consider this
example:

> "Convening educational session for pedestrian patient using pedographs
> for automatically making a topographical record challenged the nurse
> scientist while disenfranchising the penurious and impecunious."

This by no means implies that writers should avoid the use of scientific verbiage. However, elaborate, pretentious, and coy words have
no place in academic writing or in professional publications (Strunk
and White 2000). However, the line between the "fancy and the plain"
word and between the "atrocious and the felicitous" is surprisingly fine
(Strunk and White 2000, 77). Choose your "big" words wisely. Writers
should base word selection on the subject matter—nursing science versus a lite journal editorial—and the intended audience.

In this chapter, we aimed to address the importance of word choice in
manuscript development. Incorrect use of homophones and selection of
inaccurate words detracts from a written product, confusing the reader,
as do diction and syntax use errors. Word overuse, including use of "big
words" and clichés, equally diminish the quality of the narrative, further underscoring that the subject matter drives word choice.

Practice Exercises

Part A: Accurate Word Selection

Each of the following sentences contains a misused word(s). Identify and correct the word use errors:

1. The publisher injected the submission, returning it to the author with ingested revisions.

2. Academicians traditionally focus on theoretical frameworks that underwrite theses, study aims and hypothamus when conducting research.

3. The journey through graduate school inquires focus, hard work and an investigation of sweat inequity.

4. Should a naive author receive a resignation letter from a journal editor, the first thing the author should do is take a deep breath, then seek advise from someone with more publishing experience.

5. The contract implicitly stated the timeline for manuscript submission.

Part B: Learning New Words

1. Complete the entire crossword puzzle from your local newspaper for two consecutive days. Make a list of the new words learned.

2. Access and enroll is the email "word of the day" by WordGenius. Then, engage in learning one new word each day and participating in offered follow-up quizzes.

Part C: Diction Descriptive Terms

1. Access a previously written document and identify your personal word selection pattern by highlighting repeated words or words with similar meanings.

2. In the previously written document, identify the subject of the narrative, the purpose of writing the document, and the intended audience.

Part D: Using Too Many Words—Aim for Few

In the following sentence, *bracket all of the superfluous words*. Then, *prune ruthlessly*, creating a clear concise sentence(s) devoid of wordiness:

- *Nurses must function within complex and unforgiving work environments that consist of an enormous array of physical, psychological and emotional challenging demands accompanied by bullying, lateral violence, patient and family aggression, which is matched by unpredictability including inadequate staffing and long work hours that cause nurse stress, interfere with providing safe, quality care and undoubtedly contribute to medical errors and missed nursing care, all of which could benefit from practicing techniques that promote positive effects on stress.*

Part E: Avoiding Clichés

List ten Figures of speech that you found in print and commit to avoid their use in academic manuscripts and professional publications.

1.
2.
3.
4.
5.
6.
7.
8.
9.
10.

Part F: Avoid Becoming a Sesquipedalian

The following two sentences contain overly complex words, phrases, and structure. Simplify the sentences.

1. *Quantum theory suggests that change is a universe dynamic constitutive and cannot be avoided as its unforgiving constancy can only be influenced by circumstances and consequential outcomes rendering quantumness as almost counter intuitive.*

2. *In this transformational millennium between two paradigms, a leader's most pragmatic imperative is to engage fully in the obtuse realm of potential reality, anticipating change, readying for "black swans" and knowingly or unknowingly move in the same direction as the unrecognizable and unfolding change takes place.*

References

Alingod, J. 2014. 25 "Ways to Improve Your Writing Vocabulary." https://wordcounter.net/blog/2014/01/22/1027_25-ways-to-improve-your-writing-vocabulary.html.

Ashford University. n.d. "Commonly Confused Words." https://writingcenter.ashford.edu/commonly-confused-words.

Baumann, J. F., and E. J. Kameenui. 1991. "Research on Vocabulary Instruction: Ode to Voltaire." In *Handbook of Research on Teaching the English Language Arts*, edited by J. Flood, J. D. Lapp, and J. R. Squire, 604–632. New York: MacMillan.

Center for Academic Excellence 2009. "Language, tone, and audience." Retrieved from http://ww2.usj.edu/PDF/cae/toneaudience.pdf

Collins. 2016. "Kicking the habit: Analysing a writer's use of language rather than just explaining what it means!" Retrieved from http://s20211.p595.sites.pressdns.com/kicking-habit-analysing-writers-use-language-rather-just-explaining-means/

International Language Association. 2003. "Defining style." Retrieved from http://www.readwritethink.org/files/resources/lesson_images/lesson209/definition_style.pdf

Lepki, L. 2019. "The Internet's Best List of Clichés." ProWritingAid. Retrieved from https://prowritingaid.com/art/21/List-of-Clich%C3%A9s.aspx

Merriam-Webster Collegiate Dictionary. (n.d.). s.v. "diction." https://www.merriam-webster.com/dictionary/diction.

Molle, E. 2019. "Sedentary behavior and subjective well-being." (Unpublished doctoral dissertation). The Catholic University of America, Washington, DC, USA.

Orwell, G. 1946. "Politics and the English Language." *Horizon*. Vol 13, Issue 76. pp. 252–265.

Pennell, D. 2001. "A 'word' about vocabulary." Retrieved from https://education.wm.edu/centers/ttac/documents/webinars/languageinstructionsupportdocs/Lesson%209/awordaboutvocabulary.pdf

Pietroluongo, L. 2019. "Using sensory language and metaphors to boost your marketing's effectiveness." Retrieved from https://www.elegantthemes.com/blog/marketing/using-sensory-language-and-metaphors-to-boost-your-marketings-effectiveness

Pressley, M., Levin, J.R., McDaniel, M. A, 1987. "Remembering versus inferring what a word means: Mnemonic and contextual approaches." In McKeown, M. G., and Curtis, M. E. (Eds.). *The Nature of Vocabulary Acquisition*. Hillsdale, NJ, USA: Lawrence Erlbaum Associates.

ProWriting Aid. (n.d.). "The internet's best list of clichés." Retrieved from https://prowritingaid.com/art/21/List-of-Clich%C3%A9s.aspx)

School Wires. (n.d.). "Analyzing DICTION." Retrieved from https://il49000007.

schoolwires.net/cms/lib/IL49000007/Centricity/Domain/303/319-Summer-Reading-Rhetorical-Analysis-Packet.pdf

Search and Write. 2019. "Language and style." Retrieved from https://sokogskriv.no/en/writing/language-and-style/

Strunk, W., and White, E. B. 2000. *The elements of style*. (4th ed.) Upper Saddle River, NJ, USA: Pearson Education, Inc.

"Tips on Choosing the Right Words." (n.d.). Retrieved from https://grammar.yourdictionary.com/grammar/style-and-usage/choosing-the-right-word.html

University of Richmond. (n.d.). "Commonly confused words." Retrieved from http://writing2.richmond.edu/writing/wweb/conford.html

Vappingo. (n.d.). "There is a difference between the words use and utilize and you really should know it." Retrieved from https://www.vappingo.com/word-blog/there-is-a-difference-between-the-words-use-and-utilize-and-you-really-should-know-it/

Washington University Faculty. (n.d.). "Effective use of language." Retrieved from https://faculty.washington.edu/ezent/el.htm

Writing Explained (n.d.). "Principal vs. principle: What's the difference?" Retrieved from https://writingexplained.org/principal-vs-principle

Wyrick. J. 2017. *Steps to writing well*. Boston: MA, USA: Cengage Learning.

Zinsser, W.K. 2016. *On writing well*. New York, NY, USA: Harper Collins Publishers.

SECTION V

CHAPTER 11

Assuring New Nursing Knowledge Dissemination

Knowing is not enough; we must apply.
Willing is not enough; we must do.
—Johann Wolfgang von Goethe

A Writing Proficiency Crisis

WRITING well is not merely an option for nursing graduate students or those in professional practice . . . it is a necessity. Writing proficiency predicts future academic success as well as success in the nursing and healthcare industry (Graham and Perin 2007). Because literacy includes both reading and writing skills (Lexicon: Oxford Dictionary 2019), poor writing proficiency contributes to many challenges nurses face when entering graduate school programs. Although nurses may excel in the technical aspects of the Doctorate in Nursing Practice (DNP) or the PhD doctoral programs and successfully master the clinical aspects of advanced practice degree requirements, they often struggle when professors expect similar proficiency in manuscript development. It is not surprising that the three most commonly reported reasons for first-year graduate student attrition include managing time, handling heavy reading requirements, and "determining how to write on the graduate level" (Schramm-Possinger and Powers 2015, 6).

This chapter discusses writing interventions and steps to remedy writing problems during the academic and/or the professional experience. The chapter also addresses the publication process with suggestions for improving acceptance of submitted manuscripts, and handling rejection of manuscripts. Finally, we review the responsibility of advanced-degree prepared nurses to disseminate knowledge through publication in professional journals and other avenues throughout their professional careers.

The Effectiveness of Writing Interventions

Many research efforts have studied the effect of writing interventions on learning (Bangert-Drowns, Hurley, and Wilkinson 2004; Rivard 1994; Tierney 1981; Troia 2014), and the results have been inconsistent. Over thirty years ago, British educators (Britton *et al.* 1975; Martin 1984) argued that writing proficiency could improve academic learning because it "resembles processes of speaking, thinking, and learning" (Bangert-Drowns, Hurley, and Wilkinson 2004, 1). Researchers have focused on determining if "writing-to-learn models" have a positive impact on academic achievement.

As a writing intervention, writing-to-learn educational efforts require the integration of writing as an academic focus within and across academic programs (Bangert-Drowns, Hurley, and Wilkinson 2004; Troia 2014). Integration occurs by modifying teaching approaches, course requirements, rubric development, and other instructional strategies. Essentially, each course throughout the educational journey requires students to develop, enhance, and, most importantly, maintain proficiency in writing (VanDeWeghe 2005). Some educators argue that writing about course content engages students in the learning process, whereas others suggest that increasing the frequency of writing in a course without addressing the quality of the writing may not improve learning (Applebee 1984). As early as 1989, Durst and Newell highlighted the importance of the writing tasks in improving learning based on the requirement that students "review, consolidate, and retain information" (Bangert-Drowns, Hurley, and Wilkinson 2004, 31).

Other findings suggested that writing has a positive effect on learning a specific topic rather than any related course content. Langer and Applebee (1987) found that the more content in a manuscript is "manipulated" or edited, "the more likely it is to remembered and understood" (130). Banger-Drowns *et al.* (2004) reported that approximately 50% of research studies demonstrated that quality writing improves overall learning. These findings underscore the need for writers to master basic writing proficiency, which is a reflection of synthesis, organization, logical thought, and higher-order thinking.

Understanding Writing Problems

Graduate school programs focus on higher-order thinking skills and expect student manuscripts to demonstrate argumentation, reasoning, and persuasion (Rivard 1987; Troia 2014). Although it may be unrealistic to believe that writing-to-learn models are a panacea for improving student writing or learning performance, such efforts underscore the important role that effective writing plays in the learning process. Writing practices, including writing exercises, affects learning and it is "reasonable to expect some enhancement in learning from writing" (Bangert-Drowns, Hurley, and Wilkinson 2004, 51).

There is some evidence that more extensive writing projects may achieve more positive outcomes. Doctoral dissertations, evidence-based practice (EBP) projects, and capstone projects require immersion in content areas and considerable research, critical analysis, synthesis, and application. The required engagement and commitment are exceptionally intense and demand a sustained long-term focus that may prove "unmotivating or distracting for students" (Bangert-

TABLE 11.1. Scholarly Writing Problems.

Problem	Description
Writing Mechanics	Includes grammar, format, incorrect citations for source material, insufficient detail, lack of logical evidence for arguments and/or conclusions, unsuitable voice or tone, or failure to write for the intended audience.
Rhetorical Function Errors	Refer to the manner used to present and sequence content as the writing unfolds. Scholarly writing should identify the problem, underscore the problem's significance, provide research method detail, discuss results and related analysis, and articulate conclusions underpinned by the results and analysis. Without a logical flow, the reader is unable to understand the writers meaning. This includes the overuse of long, complex sentences and words used to convey sophistication, diminishing the document's clarity.
Differences in Writing Expectations	Academic scholarly writing differs from writing required in the business arena and differs further from writing expectation of journal editors. Developing flexible writing skills challenges even seasoned writers and requires time to learn and acquire proficiency.
Adhering to Principles of Style	Includes accuracy, clarity, unity, coherence and concise expression. One thought per sentences, organized paragraphs with good internal structure and logical sequencing.

Adapted from: Shaurette and Rapp 2014; MacArthur 2008; Gonyea and Anderson 2009.

Drowns, Hurley, and Wilkinson 2004, 52). Banger-Drowns, Hurley, and Wilkinson (2004) caution that writing proficiency is "differentially helpful" (53), depending on the writer's ability and relationship to the topic under discussion. This suggests that the combination of writing ability and subject matter knowledge produces complex and sometimes frustrating interactions, which suggest that graduate nursing students need to focus on improving their writing skills early in their academic journey.

Table 11.1 describes the types of writing problems experienced by graduate students. The types of problems resemble those found at the undergraduate level (Shaurette and Rapp 2014; MacArthur 2008; Gonyea and Anderson 2009).

The Importance of Graduate Student Engagement

A study by Gonyea and Anderson (2009) that analyzed the effect of writing on student learning found that "the writing that contributes most substantially to learning is the writing that engages the students in deep learning activities" (13). Figure 11.1 below illustrates the causal relationship of writing to engagement types and learning.

This model suggests that the more frequently higher order thinking skills are required in writing assignments, the more the writing advanc-

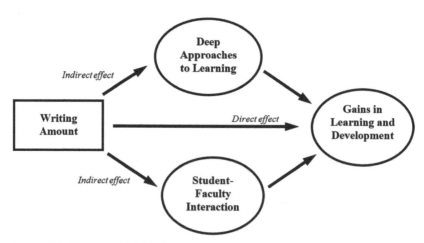

Figure 11.1. Conceptual Model for Writing, Engagement, and Learning. Source: Gonyea, R. M., Anderson, P. (2009). Writing, Engagement, and Successful Learning Outcomes in College. Paper presented at the Annual Meeting of the American Educational Research Association, San Diego, CA, April 14, 2009, p.6.

es learning. The model applies to nurses enrolled in graduate programs and to professional nurses who are engaged in knowledge dissemination through professional publication. Demanding courses can prompt graduate nursing students to engage more frequently and more intensely, which leads to improved learning. From a faculty perspective, it has been said that "expect more from graduate nursing students and you get more" (Gonyea and Anderson 2009, 13). Nurses enrolled in graduate programs may reap long-term benefits from working with professors who embed rigorous writing expectations in their courses because improved writing skills extend throughout one's professional career.

Successful Writing Interventions

For writers who want to improve their writing proficiency, or for writers with little confidence, mastering the basics of writing can advance learning and academic or professional success. Helpful writing interventions include the following (Adapted from Troia 2014 and Saver 2014):

- Complete short written content assignments or exercises that focus equally on content and adherence to writing basics. One example is the development of annotated bibliographies with critical analysis and synthesis to the topic under discussion.
- Develop a logical, clear, sufficiently detailed outline for the development of any proposed or envisioned manuscript, no matter the length.
- Reserve thirty minutes each day for writing exercises that include repeatedly editing previous work—revising and revising—to achieve clarity, conciseness, logical flow and an error-free grammatical document.
- Amass literature sources of evidence for longer assignments or manuscripts, critically review each one, and set aside those that evidence exemplar information. Focus on the exemplars in developing the envisioned document.
- Engage a colleague or family member to review and/or edit early manuscript drafts. This may provide the opportunity to re-organize content, improve logical content flow, and/or correct grammatical errors.
- Enroll in a writing workshop—online or in-person. This can re-set or refresh writing competencies, especially if the writer has not recently engaged in developing manuscripts. A host of online programs from universities and colleges, such as Stanford University, University of California—Berkley and Irvine, Arizona State University, Duke

University, and Ohio State University, are available for free and can jump-start writing interest and improve proficiency.

- Focus on "writing in the style and format" for nursing. Review top-tiered peer-review nursing journals and model writing style after published articles. Aim for a temperate, clinical tone devoid of excessive passion or flare.
- Aim to demonstrate higher-order thinking skills: critical analysis, synthesis, value determination through argumentation and justification, and application of relevant theory.
- Develop papers/projects that require idea integration or information from a variety of evidence sources.
- Consider collaborative writing with co-authors in developing, writing, and editing manuscripts for journal submission.
- Identify the topic for the dissertation, EBP project, or masters Capstone Project early. Develop that topic in course assignments across the curriculum. This enables the amassing and transference of knowledge and evidence and prepares the writer for development of the final graduate degree writing project, such as the dissertation.
- Engage in reflective learning (Anderson *et al.* 2016) by examining the strengths and weakness of the selected topic, remain open to opposing viewpoints, and strive to learn something that changes your perspective on the topic.
- Utilize software products that can assist in adhering to proper writing mechanics. These include internet resources such as Easy Writer, Grammarly, PaperRater, and Hemingway Editor.

Many writers may find it helpful to use Microsoft Words' grammar and spellcheck functions, as well as their readability statistics, which provide an analysis of a manuscript's readability based on the Flesch Reading Ease and Flesch-Kincaid Grade Level scores. The Flesch Reading Ease Score is based on the average number of syllables per word and the average number of words per sentence (Microsoft 2016). The greater the score, the easier the document is to read. For nurses who are developing educational materials for patients, the higher the score the better. Patient education materials used in federally funded research studies must adhere to specific readability standards that are monitored by university Institutional Review Boards. However, for academic work, most manuscripts should have a lower score. Aim for a score of 30, which suggests that to fully appreciate the work, the reader should have a college education.

The Flesch-Kincaid Grade Level score indicates a school grade level and is also based on the average number of syllables per word and the average number of words per sentence (Microsoft 2016). Standard writing reflects a seventh or eighth grade level (Microsoft 2016). Students should aim for a graduate level writing score of above 15.

Microsoft Word also provides the percentage of passive voice used in a document. This function aids students in assessing if their document meets graduate school expectations, which require active voice in academic writing (University of Washington 2019). The active voice focuses on the subject performing the action and immediately engages and persuades the reader, whereas the passive voice draws the reader to "action" conveyed in a sentence (CopyPress 2018).

Given the myriad of writing interventions designed to improve writing skills, how can nurses enrolled in graduate programs determine if their work meets graduate level writing expectations? Table 11.2 illustrates a set of graduate level writing proficiency indicators that can function as writing metric targets and guide nurses enrolled in masters or doctorate programs.

TABLE 11.2. Doctoral Level Indicators of Writing Proficiency.

Writing Proficiency Indicators
1. Written in active voice, not passive.
2. The absence of grammatical errors; devoid of homophones
3. 90% of narrative demonstrates strong copulative/verb use, limiting the use of "be" verbs
4. Evidence of consistent and strong complex sentence structure
5. Evident emphasis on clarity, language and syntax
6. Smooth paragraph transitions and robust middle portions of each section
7. Narrative written for the reader-who-does-not-know
8. Evidence reflective of *higher-order thinking skills* (analysis, synthesis & evaluation)
9. Use of *evidence* from the literature rather than passion to advance supposition introduces and concludes each major section of the document
10. Headings that ensure readers remain focused
11. Proofreading that eliminates all grammatical errors
12. Adherence to the current version of APA/MLA/etc. format
13. Aim for a 15 Flesch-Kincaid Grade Level, 0% passive sentences, and a reading ease score of 30

Writing for Publication: Improving Submission Acceptance

Each year, journal editors receive hundreds of article submissions that range from empirical research with clinical relevance, systematic literature reviews, theoretical analyses, and discussions to an ever-increasing number of evidenced-based practice project from DNP program graduates (Betz n.d.). Articles that receive an acceptance generally meet the following criteria suggested by Browne (2014) and Saver (2014).

The Editorial Process

Upon receipt of a submission, the journal editor or editorial team first determines if the article is a good fit with the journal's mission and audience. The editor then assesses the article for a series of indicators, including the conformance of the writing style with the journal's requirements and expectations and the currency of the literature that supports the article's content. Older articles (published more than five years in the past) must represent seminal works that are exemplars in the field. The body of the manuscript requires headings and sub-headings that logically organize the discussion for the reader, and the content should be well-developed in thought, sentence structure, and word flow. The editor assesses if the ending of one section logically transitions the reader to the next section and if the citations are cited with the correct format; this also includes Figures and tables (Browne 2014). The editor also focuses on the article's conclusions that should include a synopsis of the article, its nuances, and novel discoveries.

After the editor reviews the article, a decision to reject or proceed launches the journal's review process decision process. Figure 11.2 illustrates the general review process for peer-reviewed journals. Central to this process is the use of blinded peer review, which involves experts in the field who serve as reviewers. The journal editor assesses reviewer comments and recommendations and determines if the manuscript ranks as worthy for publication. The editor determines the depth and breadth of required edits and communicates those to the author. Once revisions are completed, the editor may request reviewers to reassess the submission and make a publication recommendation. If accepted, the submission moves on to the journal production process phase.

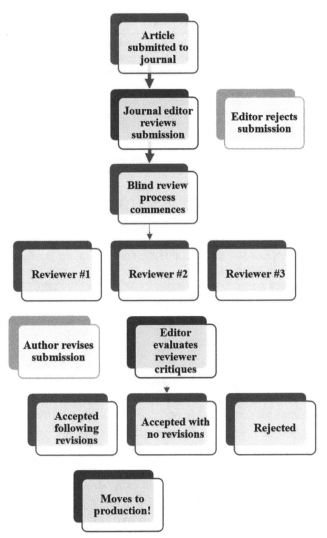

Figure 11.2. General Review Process for Peer-Reviewed Journals. Adapted from: PiscoMed Journal Review Process 2019.

Reviewer Guidelines

After a journal editor identifies a sufficiently worthy manuscript, the document is forwarded to a panel of expert reviewers. Every journal provides assessment guidelines or a rubric for their reviewers to follow as they evaluate the suitability of manuscripts for publication. Evaluation

TABLE 11.3. Examples of Journal Reviewer Guidelines.

1. What was your overall response to the manuscript? Did you like it? Does it offer contribution? Is it of use to the reader?
2. Does the Introduction provide sufficient background to underpin and advance the manuscript's topic?
3. Does it contain new ideas or issues? Does it reflect the Journal's Mission? Does it present a different focus or strategy regarding past issues or dilemmas? Is it accurate?
4. Is the manuscript structured well? Is there a logical flow of ideas? Does the author's writing style comport with Journal expectations? Is the content expressed clearly and concisely? Are the author's writing mechanics of sufficient quality? Did you find it interesting to read?
5. Do tables and figures complement the text? Any suggestions for additions or modifications?
6. Are reporting guidelines used as appropriate: CONSORT (Consolidated Standards of Reports Trials), PRISMA (Preferred Reporting Items for Systematic Reviews and Meta-Analysis), SQUIRE (Standards for Quality Improvement Reporting Excellence)
7. Are references the most relevant on the topic? Too few? Too many?
8. Does the Abstract accurately summarize the manuscript?

Adapted from: Saver 2014.

guidelines mirror the journal's mission, focus area, reading audience, and readership preferences. For example, reviewer guidelines for a journal dedicated to clinical nursing practice may significantly differ from a journal focused on finance. Authors must select the target journal wisely and understand the journal's mission and readership, as well as preferred manuscript structure, tone, and style. Reviewers take all of these and other factors into account in the manuscript evaluation process.

Table 11.3 shows guidelines used by some journals for reviewer evaluations. These examples that may prove helpful as authors strive to develop articles that meet the selected publication's standards.

Dealing with Rejection

Acceptance rates vary, although most journals rarely exceed 40%, whereas some rejection rates are as high as 97% (Mckherjee 2018; Sullivan 2015). Reasons for rejection may include the manuscript falls outside the journal's mission and scope; the writing is incomprehensible; the submission departs from the journal's style; the hypothesis is not clear; and the supporting evidence is lacking (Mckherjee 2018).

Regardless of the reason(s), the experience of rejection usually demotivates authors who truly believe their hard work represents an excellent, if not exceptional, submission. Sullivan (2015) suggests that new authors are most likely to experience rejection, although experienced authors also receive rejections.

Sullivan recommends exploring the following responses to receiving a rejection letter. First, it is best to acknowledge the feelings and regain equilibrium. Then, read the rejection letter carefully. In many cases, decision letters carefully categorize decision levels (Annesley 2011), which include the reviewer's suggestions for outright rejection: do not resubmit; declined for now, future acceptance possible; declined for now, future acceptance likely with specified revisions. The author usually receives specific details about the reasons for the decision (Annesley 2011).

Although journals differ in the amount of detail provided with reviewers' comments, any explanatory information is helpful in determining next steps. For example, a writer who failed to follow journal instructions may be encouraged to revise the document and resubmit for a successful re-submission. When a submission may be a "mismatch between the paper and the scope of the journal" (Sullivan 2015, 2), the writer might consider reviewing several issues of the journal to determine the problem. The writer may have failed to provide data or information critical to the thesis or topic under discussion, or the presentation of data may be inconclusive, may be difficult to understand, or may fail to support the findings or conclusions (Siegel and Werb 2004).

After understanding the reasons for rejection, an author may wish to review, edit, and re-submit the manuscript. Sullivan (2015) suggests that editors are "generally pleased to receive a manuscript that has been previously reviewed and revised" (4) because the re-submitted document usually reflects clearer, more concise, and better developed content. When resubmission is not successful, the author may wish to consider submitting the manuscript to another journal. Another option for authors to consider is appealing the rejection decision. The appeal should reflect an objective assessment that identifies flaws in the review process based on evidence and logic, and not emotion (Eassom 2018).

Moss (2019), a professional journal editor, offers ways to increase a publication's chances of acceptance, as illustrated below in Table 11.4.

TABLE 11.4. Ways to Increase Publication Chances.

1. Adhere to journal submission guidelines.
2. Eliminate grammatical errors & typos.
3. Do not rely on the peer review process to uncover problems.
4. Know and write for the journal's audience.
5. Polish the abstract—keep it concise, logical and clear;
6. Self-assess the article for scholarship quality, rigor, argumentation style
7. Always answer the "So what?" or Why should someone read the article?
8. Hook the reader in the introduction.
9. Focus on the logical organization of the article.
10. Imagine the audience and write for the reader who does not know.
11. Exude self-confidence, not arrogance.
12. Avoid advancing famous names unless it is central to the thesis.
13. Determine what the reader should remember most—the contribution to the field.

Adapted from: Moss 2019 and Malugani 2019.

Committing to Dissemination of Professional Knowledge

The dramatic increase in the number of nurses who are seeking graduate degrees offers the nursing profession an opportunity to advance nursing science that depends on degreed professionals making a commitment to developing and disseminating new knowledge. An exciting, scholarly adventure filled with many challenges awaits these masters and doctorate prepared nurse scientists. These challenges include the task of mastering the science of nursing and joining with scientists from other fields as equal collaborators who conduct and engage in evidence-based practice research that will advance transformation of the health-care industry. One of the most significant tasks ahead is sustaining excellence as the profession prepares nurse researchers and disseminates rigorous research findings to practice settings and clinicians (Murphy, Staffieno, and Carlson 2015).

Nursing is entering a new era and is moving from a framework that supports nursing research and developing nurse scientists to conducting investigations and to identifying the events and trends that represent the knowledge that clinicians need for practice. Never before has the importance of partnership between practitioners and researchers been as evident as now. Commitments to the linkage between academia and practice can advance practice improvements only if the expertise of those developing knowledge aligns with the experts who are leading practice innovations and developing a new knowledge base for the profession. Figure 11.3 (Murphy, Staffieno, and Carlson 2015) depicts the collaborative relationship in the practitioner-researcher partnership. The challenge to promote scholarly communication is evidence of the synergism inherent in collaborative work.

The American Association of Colleges in Nursing (AACN) addressed dissemination as a professional responsibility in their 2018 position statement, which defined the inclusivity of scholarship, underscored the scholarship of scientific inquiry and discovery, and described the promotion of scholarship. Scholarship includes knowledge generation, synthesis, and application and encompasses the dissemination of that knowledge to improve health and transformation of the healthcare industry. Communication of acquired knowledge must inform practice, education, and policy. The AACN (2015) suggests that the "hallmark attribute of scholarship is the cumulative impact of the scholar's work

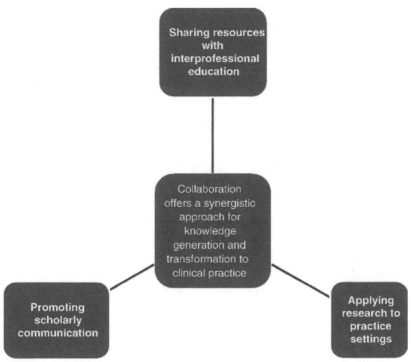

Figure 11.3. *Interconnectedness of Collaborative Efforts. Source: Murphy, Staffieno, and Carlson 2015.*

on the field of nursing and health care." (149). Examples of knowledge dissemination include:

- Dissemination in peer-reviewed journals with published impact factors or media outlets
- Presenting research, clinical programs, quality improvement initiatives, and/or practice-based findings at regional, national, and international conferences and healthcare meetings
- Communicating best practices to lay groups to promote translation and implementation of research findings,
- Publishing best practices or evaluation outcomes of doctoral-level and practice-based programs
- Providing expert review for scientific projects and journals, periodicals, or textbooks
- Creating new theoretical frameworks and theories to guide, test, and disseminate the work of the new phenomena
- Publishing to influence practice via peer-reviewed venues
- Engaging in discussion panels, journal clubs and seminars, and media interviews
- Participating in book reviews and in developing evidenced-based guidelines
- Functioning as an expert witness
- Writing letters and policy briefs to inform others of healthcare issues, concerns and services

(*Adapted from*: AACN 2018, 150–151; Hanrahan *et al.* 2010)

This chapter offered that nurses who are completing graduate degree programs, especially at the doctoral level, commit to knowledge dissemination upon entry into the program and resolve to continue doing so throughout their professional careers. With colleges and universities throughout the country producing the large number of advanced-degree prepared nurses today, the contemporary issues that are facing the healthcare industry are best addressed by those assumed to be in the most trusted profession—nurses. Knowledge dissemination at the highest level of scholarship—the nurse prepared with an advanced degree—not only is a professional privilege, but also is a major professional responsibility that all masters and doctorate prepared nurses must embrace as they progress in their respective professional journeys.

Practice Exercises

1. Define "writing-to-learn" educational writing intervention. What are the major advantages?
2. What are higher-order thinking skills?
3. How does writing enhance learning?
4. Name two scholarly writing problems.
5. Identify five successful writing interventions
6. Microsoft Words' readability statistic measures reading _____ and grade _____.
7. A graduate student should aim for a Flesch-Kincaid Grade Level score of 10. True or False?
8. Name five indicators of writing proficiency.
9. Describe the traditional steps in the journal review process.
10. Name five ways to increase publication chances.

References

AACN (American Association of Colleges of Nursing). 2018. "Defining Scholarship for Academic Nursing." *Journal of Professional Nursing* 34, 149–156. https://doi.org/10.1016/j.profnurs.2018.04.004.

Anderson, P., Anson, C.M., Gonyea, R. M., and Paine, C. 2016, December 26. "How to create high-impact writing assignments that enhance learning and development and reinvigorate WAC/WID programs: What almost 72,000 undergraduates taught us." *Across the Disciplines, 13*(4). Retrieved from https://wac.colostate.edu/docs/atd/hip/andersonetal2016.pdf

Annesley, T. 2011. "Top 10 Tips for Responding to Reviewer and Editor Comments." *Clinical Chemistry* 57 (4), 551–554.

Applebee, A. N. 1977. "Writing across the curriculum: The London Projects." *English Journal, 66*(9), 81–85. Retrieved from https://www-jstor-org.proxycu.wrlc.org/stable/pdf/815293.pdf

Bangert-Drowns, R.L., Hurley, M.M., and Wilkinson, B. (n.d.). "How does writing affect learning?" Retrieved from https://www.csun.edu/~krowlands/Content/Academic_Resources/Composition/Tool%20for%20Learning/How%20Writing%20Affects%20Learning_files/howdoes.htm

Bangert-Drowns, R.L., Hurley, M.M., and Wilkinson, B. 2004. "The effects of school-based writing-to-learn interventions on academic achievement: A meta-analysis." *Review of Educational Research, 74*(1), 29–58. Retrieved from https://doi.org/10.3102%2F00346543074001029

Betz, C. (n.d.). "Writing for publication." Retrieved from http://www.pens.org/

PENS%20Documents/PENS%202016/Handouts/Saturday%20May%2014/4A%20 Writing%20for%20Publication.pdf

Britton, J., Burgess, T., Martin, N., McLeod, A., and Rosen, H. 1975. *The development of writing abilities.* 11–18. London, UK: MacMillian.

Brownson, R. C., Eyler, A. A., Harris, J. K., Moore, J. B., and Tabak, R. G. 2018. "Getting the word out: New approaches for disseminating public health science." *Journal of Public Health Management and Practice, 24*(2), 102–111.

Browne, N. 2014. "Writing for nursing publication." *Journal of Pediatric Surgical Nursing, 3*(2), 51–57. Retrieved from https://nursing.ceconnection.com/ovid-files/01781601-201406000-00007.pdf

Colwell, J., Whittington, J., and Jenks, C. F. 2011. "Writing challenges for graduate students in engineering and technology." Paper presented at the 2-11 ASEE Annual Conference & Exposition, Vancouver, BC. Retrieved from http://www.asee.org/public/conferences/1/papers/242/download

CopyPress. 2018. "The importance of active voice in content." Retrieved from https://www.copypress.com/blog/importance-active-voice-content/

Durst, R. K., and G. E. Newell. 1989. "The uses of function: James Britton's category system and research on writing." *Review of Educational Research, 59*(4), 375–394. https://psycnet.apa.org/doi/10.2307/1170204

Eassom, H. 2018. "5 Options to consider after article rejection." Retrieved from https://www.wiley.com/network/researchers/submission-and-navigating-peer-review/5-options-to-consider-after-article-rejection

Elsevier. 2019. "How to get your research published and then noticed." Retrieved from https://www.elsevier.com/?a=91173

Gonyea, R. M., and Anderson, P. 2009, April. "Writing, engagement, and successful learning outcomes in college." Paper presented at the Annual Meeting of the American Educational Research Association, San Diego, CA, USA. Retrieved from http://cpr.indiana.edu/uploads/Gonyea-Anderson%20AERA%202009.doc

Goodman, P., Robert, R. C. & Johnson, J.E. (2020). Rigor in PhD dissertation research. *Nursing Forum.*1–10. https://doi.org/10.1111/nuf.12477

Graham, S., and Perin, D. 2007. "Writing next: Effective strategies to improve writing of adolescents in middle and high schools—A report to Carnegie Corporation of New York." Washington, DC: Alliance for Excellent Education. Retrieved from http://all4ed.org/wp-content/uploads/WritingNext.pdf

Hanrahan, K., Marlow, K., Aldrich, C., and Hiatt, A. 2010. "Dissemination of nursing knowledge: Tips and resources." Retrieved from https://nursing.uiowa.edu/sites/default/files/documents/research/templates/Disseminating%20nursing%20knowledge.pdf

Langer, J. A., and Applebee, A. N. 1987. *How writing shapes thinking.* Urbana, IL: National Council of Teachers of English. Retrieved from https://wac.colostate.edu/docs/books/langer_applebee/langer_applebee.pdf

Lexicon Dictionary. 2019. s.v. literacy. https://www.lexico.com/en/definition/literacy.

MacArthur, C. A. 2008. "Writing Disabilities: An Overview." Retrieved from http://www.ldonline.org/article/33079/

Malugani, M. 2019. "Tips for getting published in a nursing journal." Retrieved from https://www.monster.com/career-advice/article/tips-for-getting-published-in-a-nursing-journal

Microsoft. 2016. "Viewing document and readability statistics." Retrieved from https://www.officetooltips.com/word_2016/tips/viewing_document_and_readability_statistics.html

Moss, L. 2019. "25 Ways to increase your chances at publication." Retrieved from https://www.insidehighered.com/advice/2019/05/15/how-increase-your-chances-getting-your-work-published-scholarly-journal-opinion

Mukherjee, D. 2018. "11 Reasons why research papers are rejected." Retrieved from https://blog.typeset.io/11-reasons-why-research-papers-are-rejected-3e272b633186

Murphy, M. P., Staffieno, B. A., and Carlson, E. 2015. "Collaboration among DNP- and PhD-prepared nurses: Opportunity to drive positive change." *Journal of Professional Nursing, 31*(5), 388–394. Retrieved from https://www.sciencedirect.com/science/article/pii/S8755722315000320?via%3Dihub

Naber, J. and Markley, L. 2017. "A guide to nursing students' written reflections for students and educators." *Nurse Education in Practice, 25*, 1–4. Retrieved from https://doi.org/10.1016/j.nepr.2017.04.004

Nantz, S., and Britt, S. 2015. "How to get your article published." *American Nurse Today, 10*(9). Retrieved from https://www.americannursetoday.com/get-article-published/

Pisco Med Publishing 2019. "Insight: Mathematics." Retrieved from http://insight.piscomed.com/index.php/MTA/about/editorialPolicies

Rivard, L.P. 1994. "A review of writing to learn in science: Implications for practice and research." *Research Journal of Research in Science Teaching, 31*(9), 969–983. Retrieved from https://doi.org/10.1002/tea.3660310910

Roush, K. 2017. "Beginning a published writer." *American Journal of Nursing, 117*(3), 63–66. Retrieved from https://journals.lww.com/ajnonline/Fulltext/2017/03000/Becoming_a_Published_Writer.33.aspx#print-article-link

SAGE Connection. 2013. "9 Publishing basics for anyone submitting to a scholarly journal." Retrieved from http://connection.sagepub.com/wp-content/uploads/2013/10/Publishing-blog-post.jpg

Saver, C. 2014. *Anatomy of writing for publication for nurses.* (2nd ed.). Indianapolis, IN, USA: Sigma Theta Tau International.

Schramm-Possinger, M.E., and Powers, D.E. 2015. *The first year of graduate study: Documenting challenges and informing ways to reduce attrition.* Princeton, NJ, USA; Educational Testing Service. Retrieved from https://www.ets.org/Media/Research/pdf/RM-15-02.pdf

Shaurette, M., and Rapp, R. 2014, June 15–18. "Overcoming the writing challenges of students in a distance delivery technology master of science program." Paper presented at the 121st ASEE Annual Conference& Exposition. Retrieved from https://www.asee.org/public/conferences/32/papers/8422/download

Siegel, V., and Werb, Z. 2004. "Career advice for life scientists II: How to read and respond to a journal rejection letter." Bethesda, MD, USA: The American Society for

Cell Biology. 156–160. Retrieved from http://www.bumc.bu.edu/facdev-medicine/files/2011/11/Career-Advice-for-Life-Scientists-II-ASCB.pdf

Sullivan, G. 2015. "What to do when your paper is rejected." *Journal of Graduate Medical Education, 7*(1), 1–3. Retrieved from https://doi.org/10.4300/JGME-D-14-00686.1

Tierney, R.J., Soter, A., O'Flahavan, J.F., and McGinley, W. 1989. "The effects of reading and writing upon thinking critically." *Reading Research Quarterly, 24*, 2, 134–173. Retrieved from https://psycnet.apa.org/doi/10.2307/747862

Troia, G. 2014. Evidence-based practices for writing instruction. Retrieved from http://ceedar.education.ufl.edu/wp-content/uploads/2014/09/IC-5_FINAL_08-31-14.pdf

University of Washington. 2019. Teaching with Microsoft Word. Retrieved from https://english.washington.edu/teaching/teaching-microsoft-word

VanDeWeghe, R. 2005. "Research matters: What are the effects of writing-to-learn programs?" *English Journal, 95*(2). Retrieved from http://www.csun.edu/~krowlands/Content/Academic_Resources/Composition/Tool%20for%20Learning/Research-WAC%20from%20EJ.pdf

CHAPTER 12

The Importance of Collaboration

Alone we can do so little; together we can do so much.
—Helen Keller

Introduction

IN health care today, nurses typically collaborate with a large network of colleagues, partners, associates, customers, and patients. But in our writing endeavors, we collaborate with a much smaller, far more specialized network of individuals, who like us, are professionals who are involved in and committed to generating research and disseminating research results through traditional communication channels. This communication network includes other authors whose previous work provides the evidence for our theses and suppositions; peers who are working to complete advanced degrees in nursing; nursing colleagues who are joining together to publish an article in a nursing journal or to write a business plan for a new nursing enterprise; editors of nursing journals; librarians; and independent experts who provide specialized assistance with writing and editing. Although the nature of collaboration within this network varies with the end product, the overall success of the collaboration is critical to the future of the nursing profession which, as we discussed in Chapter 1, depends upon our ability to generate a continual pipeline of high-quality nursing research *and* publications that disseminate the findings. As Charles Darwin advised so many years ago, it is those who have learned to collaborate and improvise that have most effectively prevailed in the history of man.

According to Merriam-Webster (2019), the term collaboration has its root in Latin from the prefix com, which means "with, together, or jointly," which was then combined with *laborare*, "to labor," to form *collaborare*, or "to labor together." In this chapter, we review the benefits and challenges of collaboration, and we describe the different types of collaboration that occur between and among the various members of the communications network that support professional publications in nursing.

Writing as a Group

In nursing today, it is common for teams of nurses to collaborate on writing an article for a professional nursing journal. As shown below in Table 12.1, writing as a group has many benefits and challenges.

Successful collaborative writing requires adherence to some basic rules. Frassl *et al.* (2018) suggest that the collaborative process begins with building the writing team based on the expertise of the team members, commitment to the writing project, and availability of the team

TABLE 12.1. Collaborative Writing: Benefits and Challenges.

Pros	Cons
1. Multiple experts are better than one for idea generation and development.	1. Requires complex communication, attention to detail and effective singular leadership in overseeing the project.
2. A self-directed and engaged group may more rapidly complete the task.	2. Unproductive conflict based on differences in opinions can present an obstacle to getting the job done.
3. The product may provide more value, wisdom and expertise.	3. Expectations may differ and generate misunderstandings regarding writing, editing, and publishing the written work.
4. Creditability improves when at least one co-author possesses subject matter expertise.	4. Expense-sharing could morph into a group stumbling block.
5. Each author spends less time writing.	5. Differing tones and voice equal unevenness requiring re-work.
6. A co-author's publisher connections may speed up proposal approval.	6. If a book is the product, inconsistent chapter format requires serious editing and/or revision.
7. Each author can assist the other with getting beyond "writing blocks".	7. Liability in the form of author plagiarism affects all co-authors.
8. Enables timeline development with hard-stop submission deadlines.	8. Should the collaboration deteriorate, each author will wrestle with ownership and the freedom to use content at will.
9. Promotes diversity, equity and inclusion.	

Adapted from: Tener 2013; Frassl *et al.* 2018.
Creative Commons license link https://creativecommons.org/licenses/by/4.0/.

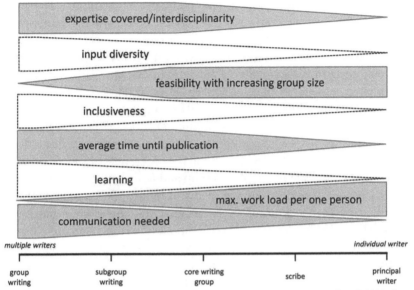

Figure 12.1. *Decision chart for (collaborative) writing strategy. Source: Frassl et al. 2018. Creative Commons license link https://creativecommons.org/licenses/by/4.0/.*

members given the timeline for completion. Figure 12.1 depicts a decision chart that recognizes the importance of interdisciplinary expertise, diversity, inclusivity, group size, and co-author workload, as well as the importance of transparent communication when engaging multiple writers in the writing process.

At this early stage of a writing group's development, it is critical to make decisions about the order of authors. Determining the order is an early, essential task of the writing group that helps to avoid confusion and discord later in the process. Such decisions determine not only the nature and extent of each author's contribution, but also citation statistics and author rankings that favor the first three authors of a publication and influence scientific and academic promotions, appointments, and funding (Zhou *et al.* 2007).

The American Psychological Association (APA) (2017) states that only those who have significantly contributed to a publication should be listed as an author. Thus, *principal authorship* must reflect the value and depth of the contribution, not the status of the author, according to the APA. This is most relevant for research collaborators who have been awarded grant funding and who may utilize research assistants to generate data and data analysis. The International Committee of Medical Journal Editors (ICMJE) has also developed criteria for authorship. These include substantial contribution to the work, including design, analysis, and interpretation of findings; drafting; revising for scholarly content; accepting accountability for integrity of the work; and author confidence in the work of coauthors (ICMJE 2019).

Beyond authorship, Frassl *et al.* (2018) suggest that the group must set timelines that include firm and "final deadlines," (3) which allow ample time for review and multiple revisions of the manuscript. This involves discussing and deciding upon the different levels of collaboration that are possible in a writing group and *how* the work of the group will be accomplished. As shown below in Figure 12.2, a range of possibilities exist when working within a collaborative writing group.

As shown in Table 12.2, the collaborative writing process of prewriting, planning, conducting research, drafting/writing, revising, and editing and proofreading differs little from individual author manuscript development. However, it can be far more complex given individual coauthor interests. These stages require a realistic schedule that allows adequate time for sharing document drafts, reviewing documents, offering substantive feedback, and completing revisions. What this also means for busy nurses is that writing as part of a group is an essential obligation to the nursing profession that requires considerable time, commitment, and planning.

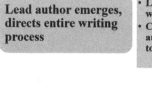

Lead author emerges, directs entire writing process	• Lead author conducts literature search and writes article draft • Co-authors review draft individually and lead author creates final draft and submits article to journal
Lead author organizes writing sessions with timelines	• Some co-authors conduct research for literature search • Document drafted by all authors during writing sessions, and then submitted to lead author for review and submission to journal

Figure 12.2. Options for Collaborative Writing.

TABLE 12.2. *Traditional Collaborative Writing Phases.*

Phase	Key Components
Pre-Writing	Through brainstorming, the group understands & agrees on the task and envisioned product; the group drafts a thesis statement.
Development	Manuscript sections identified and assigned to coauthors. Deadlines set with allocated periods for group revision & editing.
Searching for Evidence	Group agrees on evidence sources, information screening process, and critical analysis plan.
Drafting/Writing	Clarity regarding style, tone, and format determined; authors aim for clarity, logical flow, concise development of thought
Revising	Group prioritizes logical progression of ideas and addresses flow of information first. Then, addresses structure, style, and tone, ensuring they reasonably match.
Editing & Proofreading	Each co-author provided with sufficient time to edit for formatting, technical writing errors, sentence structure, typos.

Adapted from: University of North Carolina Chapel Hill 2019 and Frassl *et al.* 2018.

Leadership Matters

In addition to the important tasks of dividing the workload of tasks and adhering to a strict work schedule, the success of a writing group depends upon the emergence of a strong leader who will assume overall responsibility for the entire process of drafting, meeting deadlines, proofreading, and submitting the article to a professional journal. Although some of tasks will be completed by others on the writing team, it is the leader who oversees, reminds, supports, and steps in when hands-on support is needed (Khoo 2012). This includes managing version control, in which each version of a draft is carefully dated and labeled to identify each co-author's edits. The leader often develops a first draft of the manuscript and forwards it to coauthors for editing and feedback (Khoo 2012). This enables a synthesis of the co-authors' contribution and development of a manuscript that finds a balance between different writing styles (Khoo 2012). The strong leader of a writing group creates momentum, generates enthusiasm for the process and end product, arbitrates misunderstandings within the team, serves as the primary contact with journal editors, and facilitates a high level of collaborative engagement that generates to the intended result—a publishable product.

Selecting a Publication

One of the most important decisions of a writing group is selecting the most appropriate professional journal for their article. Given the large number of available nursing journals, nurses who are new to publishing often find this decision to be a daunting one. Although the ultimate decision typically rests with the lead author, some members of the writing group can collect information about different journals that will help the group make a wise decision. Here are our suggestions for actions that will help your team identify the most appropriate journal:

1. *Visit the journal's website.* There is important information on these websites, such as descriptions of the journal's reading audience, publication schedule, and author guidelines that specify critical formatting directions, publication style (such as the APA), and directions for online submission.

2. *Analyze the journal's archives.* These archives of past issues provide the best evidence about a professional journal. We suggest reviewing the contents of the journal for at least the past five years. This review should include identifying the reading audience (e.g., nurse clinicians, nursing educators, nursing administrators); the journal's focus on practice vs. research; content areas; required format (discussion, opinion/editorial, or a research format with objectives, methods, results, and implications); and the tone of the writing (formal vs. conversational).

3. *Consider the journal's impact factor.* This metric was originally used by libraries as a helpful aid for identifying the most influential journals to purchase for their collections (Garfield 2006). The calculation is simple: the impact factor (IF) is the average number of times a journal's articles are cited over a two-year period. Although the calculation is simple, its meaning is not. According to Sharma (2014), as an indicator of a journal's importance to its field, the IF is widely used as a proxy for a publication's value but is often misunderstood because it does not reflect the quality of a journal's content. Other scientists have argued that the number is misleading because it relies on an average, whereas others have concluded that "no single number can capture the worth of a scientist's work" (Bohannon 2016, 1). Yet publishing in a prestigious journal can increase academic success. Given the controversies about the IF in academia, the best advice to a writing group of

nurses is to consider the IF of a nursing journal as only one factor in making the important decision about the best journal for their manuscript.

4. *Contact the journal editor.* After making a preliminary decision about a journal, a writing group may be unsure if their manuscript is appropriate for a particular journal. Some journal editors welcome direct inquiries about the appropriateness of a potential manuscript, whereas others request that the corresponding author submit a summary of the proposed article for the editor to review. Correspondence with journal editors is the responsibility of the writing group's lead author, who is usually designated as the "corresponding author" of a manuscript. (See section below about working with journal editors.)

Ethical Concerns

Co-authorship in academic publications can raise concerns about integrity in the publication process. Anderson (2014) cautions collaborators to be cognizant of the ethical implications associated with co-authorship. Each author assumes the responsibility to ensure at the content they contribute—data analysis, critical analysis, and synthesis of evidence—is accurate and truthful. Professional publications are obligated to reject writing that includes false or deceptive statements, or inaccurate data. Publications are also obligated to retract published articles in which significant errors are found and to publicly acknowledge the retraction in the journal.

Another concern for any writing group is *plagiarism*, which has its roots from the Latin word *plagiarus* for "kidnapper" defined by Merriam-Webster (n.d.) as the wrongful act of [kidnapping] the product of another person's mind and presenting it as your own. Plagiarism includes reproducing portions of someone else's published or unpublished material; using their "intellectual property," i.e., their original words, ideas, images, or creative expressions, and representing them as one's own thinking without acknowledging the original source; failing to use quotation marks; and failing to obtain an author's permission for reproducing a major piece of their work (Johnson 2016). An author who uses the work of another and represents it as their own has committed plagiarism, which violates ethical standards.

According to technology experts (Johnson 2019), concerns about plagiarism in academia and publishing, as well as improvements in search engine technology, have stimulated the development of plagiarism detectors that can screen text for spelling and grammar errors, adherence to a particular publication style (such as APA), and most importantly, similarities with other texts that may represent plagiarism. These detectors can identify such similarities with both speed and accuracy, which according to Johnson, can reduce the risk of plagiarism by up to 99%.

Working with Journal Editors

Nurses work with many collaborators, and among the most important are the editors of professional journals (Sharp 2014). According to prior research by McGinty (1999), journal editors serve as "gatekeepers who funnel manuscripts in one direction or another, or rejecting materials entirely." (1). In this role, McGinty suggested, journal editors are continuing a credentialing system that has evolved from the guild system of the Middle Ages. Even in this era of the internet, when vast amounts of information are freely accessible and have eroded some of their power, these editors continue to have an "impact on the professional life of every scholar, . . ." (McGinty 1999). "Establishing scholarly credentials is crucial in higher education," said McGinty (1999, 2). As we stated earlier, this is especially true for nurses who are seeking academic promotions or research funding.

Journal editors serve as the primary contact for the corresponding authors of manuscripts. These editors have the critical responsibility of ensuring the quality of publications in their journal through the blinded, peer review process. By necessity, editors maintain very large networks of content experts who serve their journal as voluntary peer reviewers. Editors rely on these collaborators to judge each manuscript's quality and the acceptability of the manuscript for publication and to provide timely reviews of manuscripts. Serving as a peer reviewer is a professional obligation of experts with recognized experience in a field of study.

Editors typically create their own guidelines for reviewers. Shown in Table 12.3 is a set of general questions about peer review that can be useful for both reviewers and authors.

For nursing and other professional disciplines, the process of professional, blinded peer review is essential for ensuring the quality of professional publications, preventing the publication of poor quality or plagiarized work, and maintaining a high level of trust in the peer-

TABLE 12.3. Effective Peer Review.

Issue Category	Peer Review Questions
Introduction	• Does the introduction hook the reader? • Is the condition that gives rise to the topic sufficiently supportive? • Does it comfortably transition the reader to the topic narrative?
Topic Statement	• Is the topic statement clear and concise? • Has the writer articulated the significance of the argument?
Organization & Rhythm	• How do ideas progress throughout the manuscript? • Does the writer offer transitions connecting paragraphs?
Analysis of Evidence	• Is every element of evidence analyzed? • Does the writer use too many quotes instead of paraphrasing? • Is the writer's vantage point of the topic sufficiently supported? • Does the writer make unsubstantiated statements? • Would an opposing viewpoint enrich the narrative?
Citation	• Is the writer following the correct format? • Are all outside sources cited? • Are in-text citations missing?
Conclusion	• Does the conclusion introduce new information and open new questions? • Does it make the topic appear more complex compared to narrative content? • Does it summarize the main points of the manuscript? • Does it reinforce the writer's viewpoint or argument?

Adapted from: Shuttleworth 2019b, Lone Star CyFair Writing Center 2013.

reviewed journals (Shuttleworth 2019a). Peer-reviewed journals are highly respected as purveyors of critical information, which advances knowledge and professional progress. Disadvantages of the peer review process include the lengthy time required for the review process and the lack of a standardized grading system (Shuttleworth 2019b). In addition, in the blinded peer review process, authors are not able to judge the expertise or potential bias of the journal's reviewer panel.

The journal editor typically sends the corresponding author of a manuscript either the reviewers' verbatim comments or a summary of the comments, and their recommendations to the journal for either accepting the manuscript "as is" (which is rare), with corrections (which is common), or totally rejecting the manuscript, which unfortunately, is also very common (Lone Star CyFair Writing Center 2013). This feedback from reviewers is important for two reasons. *First*, the suggested corrections from reviewers provide the explicit directions for improving the manuscript, which not only helps the authors improve their writing skills, but also increases the likelihood that the quality of their manuscript will improve sufficiently and lead to publication. *Second*, the reviewers' feedback provides the rationale for the journal's rejection of manuscripts that are poor in quality.

The journal editor serves as the intermediary between corresponding authors and reviewers. After receiving the reviewers' comments, it is the responsibility of the lead author of the manuscript to ensure that all corrections are completed according to the feedback and timeline set by the editor. In collaboration, the journal editor monitors the corrected manuscripts and ensures that all corrections have been made before accepting a manuscript.

Working with Librarians

Those of us who direct graduate programs, supervise graduate research, and mentor graduate students have offered the same sage advice to brand new graduate students: *identify your university's research librarian who specializes in your area of chosen study and develop a strong, collaborative relationship with this very important individual at the university*. This advice is based on a realistic appraisal of the information world of today, which is vastly more complex in the era of the internet, and the critical need for graduate students to develop "information literacy." According to the American Library Association's (ALA) Information Literacy Competency Standards for Higher Education (2000), information literacy is "a set of skills that enables a person to navigate the universe of information, and to make sense of unfiltered formats, raising questions about its authenticity, validity, and reliability." The ALA (2000) concluded that "the sheer abundance of information will not in itself create a more informed citizenry without a complementary cluster of abilities necessary to use information effectively" (1).

In her review of the role of librarians in academic success, Dold (2013) found that although today's college students may have a high level of computer literacy, they typically struggle with determining the quality of the tsunami of information that is one click on the internet or one Google search away. Because abundance of information does not mean that all information is useful for scholarship, Dold (2013) said, academic success today depends upon the students' "abilities to evaluate the information that they can access, understand the quality of their information sources, and to organize diverse sources into a coherent theme," (2).

Dold's description of today's librarians as gatekeepers, teachers, scholars, and collaborators matches our own professional experience working at many different universities with these most valuable collaborators. As Dold (2013) summarized:

> Whereas fifty years ago they created collections of reliable paper-based resources, they now also teach students how to think about a research problem, how to recognize their information needs, how to evaluate the information they collect from a bewildering variety of sources, and how to use that information responsibly. (2)

As we discussed in Chapter 3, the quality of nursing research depends on nurses' ability to conduct expert literature reviews. The quality of a literature review is directly related to the reviewer's ability to critically assess the quality of prior research and to recognize the nuances that distinguish high quality research (Sovacool, Axsen, and Sorrella 2018). The message for nursing educators is that, at the beginning and throughout graduate school, masters and doctoral students need significant training to increase their higher-order thinking skills and work with information at the level needed for academic success. Such important training—whether provided through discussions in the classroom, demonstrations in the university library, or coaching—is best facilitated by a strong partnership between the nursing faculty and their expert, and often under-utilized and under-appreciated, collaborators in the university library.

Working with Independent Writing Experts

Given the challenges of writing, many students have hired professional editors to edit academic manuscripts including capstone projects, EBP reports, and doctoral dissertations. These experts are usually independent professionals who work for and report directly to the student, who pays their fees, and not the student's university. Because the relationship between the student and the editor is a confidential one, editors do not acknowledge their student clients and they refrain from any discussions of the student's work with anyone but the student.

Professional editing has a number of benefits including an immediate improvement in writing quality, clarity, readability, flow, and adherence to style standards. Professional editors have the advantage of objectivity in making editorial decisions, and they also provide a fresh eye for the text, which students typically lack after working on a document for so long, making so many revisions, and creating numerous drafts. Manuscript Editor Online (2019) suggests that professional editors reduce author stress, frustration, and the time that authors labor on correcting grammar and trying unsuccessfully to improve their writing style. The outcome of a professionally-edited document is an error-free, grammatically-perfect text without typographical errors, homophones (words that are spelled the same but have different meanings), inappropriate words, colloquial terms, and poor transitions; and with perfect adherence to the style guidelines of the APA, which are required for nursing and other social science publications. Use of a writing expert can also increase publisher acceptance of manuscripts, decrease requests for revision, and ultimately, shorten the timeline to publication.

Professional editing is an additional cost for graduate students, but beyond the immediate benefits, there are long-term benefits. Working with a professional editor can be beneficial in disseminating knowledge throughout one's professional career. Working with the same editor over time builds rapport and a familiarity with your style and expectations, which ultimately shortens the entire editing process.

Drinkwater (2018) offered suggestions for selecting a professional editor that include contracting with an editor who specializes in the author's field (in this case, nursing), is familiar with the audience and requirements of nursing journals and textbook publishers, and understands topics that are most attractive to professional journals and publishers. When considering an editor, it is helpful to discuss your expectations about the editing, and whether it will include changes in grammar and style, content, or both. It is helpful to ask for references from other students who have utilized the editor's services. You can also request a sample edit of a short piece of narrative that you created.

From a contractual standpoint, it is helpful if there is a written agreement between the student and the editor. This agreement should include the limits of the editing (grammatical or content or both), expectations of the turnaround time, product (document with tracked changes for the student's file and/or a clean copy), expected fees and payment schedule, and deadlines. It is also critical to discuss if the editing fees include or exclude additional changes that are requested after the first round of editing or after the faculty review. This is especially important with work on dissertations, which typically involve many revisions.

Taylor (2017), a professional editor, offers several tips for nurse authors who serve as their own editors. One suggestion is not to rely on suggested corrections about spelling and grammar from word processing programs. Homophones may escape detection and the program may erroneously replace a correct comma with a semi-colon. Another recommendation is to read the manuscript from the end to the beginning, in the hope that this will highlight spelling and grammatical errors. However, the best editing approach, when electing not to use the services of an editing expert, is partnering with a peer, which we discuss in the next section.

Editing with Peers

Peer editing might seem somewhat intimidating, but it is one of the best ways for all writers to improve their own writing skills. This type of collaboration presents a wonderful opportunity for writers to assist each other while reaching their full potential (University of Connecticut 2019). More specifically, peer editing can help writers:

- Read manuscripts more carefully, with attention to writing details;
- Achieve improved writing skills by appreciating the perception of reviewers whose objectivity is so valuable in the review process;
- Provide constructive feedback on another author's work;
- Respond to feedback through editing and revising their own work.

Peer editors can use the information in Table 12.3 as a helpful framework for reviewing a colleague's writing. But in our experience working with new writers, there are two types of peer editing that are most helpful to nurses. The first and most useful in what we call scrubbing, which as the term suggests, means cleaning up your article (Hoffman and Hoffman 2003). With this powerful peer editing technique, this process is done in pairs who work together in a very low-tech way—each with a printed copy of the text and a red pen—and with each taking turns to slowly read the paragraphs of the text aloud. Through this process of ear editing, peers are able to check the writing for grammar, spelling, and punctuation errors that may be missed by simply reading the text, as well as identifying tangents, passive voice, indecisive terms, colloquial words or slang, contractions, euphemisms, offensive words, noun strings, pronouns if they are not permitted by the required style guide, and other issues with the manuscript's sequencing, voice, and tone.

This collaborative process allows you to hear problems that "our eyes alone cannot detect" (Nordquist, 2019, 1), or as UNC's Writing Center (2019) said, the reading aloud technique helps the brain receive information in a different way that allows listeners to notice areas that may need revision. Areas in the text that simply do not sound right, usually are not, say the experts. Although UNC also suggests the use of text-to-speech software as an alternative to peer editing, we recommend peer editing because in our diverse experience working with many nurses, it is a collaborative, collegial, easy, and effective proofing technique that promotes teamwork among nurses and truly improves the quality of nurses' writing.

The second type of peer editing that is very helpful is working in dyads to double check the accuracy of the bibliography in an academic paper or a dissertation. Writers can certainly use the search function in their software to check to be sure that all authors in the text are listed in the bibliography, and all citations in the bibliography are in the text. Writers can also use software that assures compliance with APA publication guidelines (Johnson 2019). However, given the well-known challenges with formatting citations in nursing papers and publications, peer editing can be a very effective, efficient approach for confirming the bibliography and also assuring that all references are formatted properly according to the APA, MLA/etc. style guidelines. Again, this process uses reading aloud to confirm the congruence between references in the text and in the bibliography and to review the formatting of all references.

This chapter focused on the opportunity that collaborative writing brings to authors interested in working with colleagues who shared subject matter interest and expertise. While the discussion noted the benefits of working with multiple authors, it also acknowledged the challenges that can emerge with working with diverse experts. Collaborative writing options guided the discussion as well as the collaborative writing phases in which multiple authors engage. Ethical concerns rounded out the discussion with specific reference to plagiarism, the peer review and editing process, and working with independent writing experts.

Practice Exercises

Questions to refresh content discussion:

1. Identify three benefits of collaboration
2. Name four challenges associated with collaborative co-authorship
3. Identify the ten simple rules for writing a multi-authored paper.
4. What does the APA state regarding principal authorship?
5. How does a lead author emerge in collaborative writing?
6. What are the six collaborative writing phases?
7. Name four steps in the journal selection process.
8. Define plagiarism.
9. Is copying your own published work considered plagiarism?
10. Is copying your own unpublished work considered plagiarism?

The Journal editorial review process:

The following chart represents a typical journal editorial review process discussed in Chapter 11. Fill in the blanks.

References

American Library Association 2000. "Information Literacy Competency Standards for Higher Education." Chicago, IL: American Library Association. https://alair.ala.org/handle/11213/7668.

American Psychological Association (APA). 2017. "Ethical principles of psychologists and code of conduct." Retrieved from https://www.apa.org/ethics/code/

Anderson, H. 2014. "Co-Author Responsibility: Distinguishing Between the Moral and Epistemic Aspects of Trust." *European Molecular Biology Organization* (*EMBO*) *Reports* 15 (9), 914–918.

Bohannon, J. 2016. "Hate journal impact factors?" New study gives you one more reason. Retrieved from https://www.sciencemag.org/news/2016/07/hate-journal-impact-factors-new-study-gives-you-one-more-reason

Merriam-Webster's Collegiate Dictionary. (n.d.) s.v., "collaborate." http://www.merriam-webster.com/dictionary/collaborate.

Dold, C.J. 2013. "The role of librarians in academic success." 2013. *Academic Services Faculty and Staff Publications, 157.* Tampa, FL: University of South Florida. Retrieved from https://scholarcommons.usf.edu/cgi/viewcontent.cgi?article=1157&context=tlas_pub

Drinkwater, K. 2018. "How to choose and use editors for your self-published nooks."

Retrieved from https://selfpublishingadvice.org/writing-how-to-choose-and-use-editors-for-your-self-published-books/

Frassl M.A., Hamilton D.P., Denfeld B.A., de Eyto E., Hampton S.E., Keller P.S., *et al.* 2018. "Ten simple rules for collaboratively writing a multi-authored paper." *PLoS Comput Biol, 14* (11): e1006508. Retrieved from https://doi.org/10.1371/journal.pcbi.1006508

Garfield, E. 2006) "The history and meaning of the journal impact factor." *JAMA, 295*: 90–93.

Han, Y., Zhou, B. Pei, J., and Jia, Y. 2009. "Understanding importance of collaborations in co-authorship networks: A supportiveness analysis approach." Proceedings of the 2009 SIAM International Conference on Data Mining. Retrieved from https://epubs.siam.org/doi/abs/10.1137/1.9781611972795.95

Hoffman, G. and Hoffman, G. 2003. *Adios, Struck and White*. (3rd ed.). Huntington Beach, CA: Verve Press.

International Committee of Medical Journal Editors (ICMJE). 2019. "Defining the role of authors and contributors." Retrieved from: http://www.icmje.org/recommendations/browse/roles-and-responsibilities/defining-the-role-of-authors-and-contributors.html

Johnson, J. 2019. "Top 5 best plagiarism checking tools in 2019." Retrieved from https://www.techtimes.com/brandspin/238059/20190130/top-5-best-plagiarism-checking-tools-2019.htm

Johnson, J. E. 2016. "Academic integrity, plagiarism & fair use: Principles guiding your academic program." PowerPoint Slide Presentation. Washington, DC: The Catholic University of America, Conway School of Nursing.

Khoo, T. 2012. "Making co-writing work." *The research whisperer*. Retrieved from https://researchwhisperer.org/2012/01/21/co-writing/

Lone Star CyFair Writing Center. 2013. "What is peer review?" Retrieved from http://www.lonestar.edu/departments/tutoring/Scholarly_Sources.pdf

Manuscript Editor Online. 2019. "Benefits of professional editing." Retrieved from http://www.mseditoronline.com/benefits.html

McGinty, S. 1999. *Gatekeepers of knowledge: Journal editors in the sciences and the social sciences*. Westport, CT: Greenwood Publishing Group, Inc. Retrieved from https://www.google.com/search?tbo=p&tbm=bks&q=inauthor:%22Stephen+McGinty%22

Nordquist, R. 2019. "Collaborative writing." Retrieved from https://www.thoughtco.com/what-is-collaborative-writing-1689761

Merriam-Webster's Collegiate Dictionary. (n.d.) s.v., "plagiarism." http://www.merriam-webster.com/dictionary/plagiarism.

Sharma, M., Sarin, A. , Gupta, P., Sachdeva, S., and Desai, A.V. 2014. "Journal impact factor: Its use, significance, and limitations." *World Journal of Nuclear Medicine* 13(2): 146.

Shuttleworth, M. 2019a. "Disadvantages of peer reviews." Retrieved from https://explorable.com/disadvantages-of-peer-reviews

Shuttleworth, M. 2019b. "Advantages of Peer Reviews." Retrieved from https://explorable.com/advantages-of-peer-reviews

Sparks, S.C. 2014. "From gatekeepers to facilitators: Understanding the role of the journal editor." *College English 77* (2): 153–157

Sovacool, B. K., Axsen, J., and Sorrella, S. 2018. "Promoting novelty, rigor, and style in energy social science: Towards codes of practice for appropriate methods and research design." *Energy Research & Social Science, 4*, 12–42. Retrieved from https://doi.org/10.1016/j.erss.2018.07.007

Tener, l. 2013. "Should I have a co-author? Pros and cons of collaborating on a book." Retrieved from https://www.lisatener.com/2013/06/should-i-have-a-co-author-pros-and-cons-of-collaborating-on-a-book/

University of Connecticut. 2019. "Collaborative writing resources." Retrieved from https://writingcenter.uconn.edu/collaborative-writing-resources/#

University of North Carolina: Chapel Hill. 2019. "Group writing." Chapel Hill, NC: The Writing Center. Retrieved from https://writingcenter.unc.edu/tips-and-tools/group-writing/%20Review.pdf

Zhou, D., Orshanskiy, S.A., Zha, H., and Glies, C. L. 2007. "Co-ranking authors and documents in a heterogeneous network." Retrieved from https://clgiles.ist.psu.edu/papers/ICDM2007-corank-hetero-networks_long.pdf

Index